Praise for *Lo*

"I consider this to be one of the most outstanding books on Alzheimer's I have ever read."
Michael A. Breiner, M.D.

Love is Ageless is truly unique and serves as a landmark volume. It is a valuable resource."
Andrew N. Wilner, M.D., FACP

"Beautiful and poignant! A MUST reading for my patients."
Janice B. Dorn, M.D., Ph.D.

"For the emotional and aesthetic value of the selections, the useful information on Alzheimer's, and the Resources and Bibliography sections, this book is well worth reading and keeping as a reference."
National Council of Senior Citizens

"This is an altogether rewarding book. For those enmeshed in the struggle it says, 'you are not alone.' To those outside looking on, it brings understanding and compassion."
Senior Scene, Tacoma, Washington

"The blend of poetry and short stories makes for a lively, diverse collection which is never too predictable in format and approach. It presents patients as individuals with their own joys and unique perspectives. A fine approach to a topic often considered from an impersonal perspective of gloom and depression."
The Midwest Review of Books

"We think the stories in *Love Is Ageless* will surprise you. While they reveal a disease that is almost symbiotic in its suffering, the stories are not about that suffering, but about understanding. These people have gone someplace most of us have not, and they have learned something of which all of us have need."
The Monthly, Berkeley, California

"These accounts are vivid, moving, and alive. The mystery of Alzheimer's loses its remoteness and takes on the bittersweet tragedy of real people struggling to communicate love and understanding under the most difficult circumstances. This book will serve as a great consolation to those caught up in the net of this affliction, and will instruct those unfamiliar with it far better than any dozen other books."

Howard Schwartz, author of *REIMAGINING THE BIBLE*: The Storytelling of the Rabbis

"This collection reminds us of the fragile nature of our existence and that we, too, will grow old and die someday. We are charged with interacting objectively with those who suffer from the disease, rather than viewing them with detachment, or even worse, with sentimentality. Several of the stories develop these ideas with clear, straightforward characterization and plotting."

Minnesota Gerontologist

"This anthology is uplifting and informative, compassionate and humorous."

Elderly Health Services Newsletter

"If people ask you what it's like loving an Alzheimer's patient, give them this book – it puts feelings into words."

Jane Heald, Former Executive Director of the National Support Center for Families of the Aging

"The writings reveal observations recorded honestly. They show tenderness, surprise, hope, despair, disappointment, heartache, challenges, pleasures and victories. Sometimes there is joy, expectancy, and happiness. I found it touching and deeply moving. It is hard to imagine that a tragic disease can result in pleasant reading – pleasant because of good writing, but also because the reader sees loving, patient care given to people who need it."

Senior Life

Love Is Ageless

STORIES ABOUT
ALZHEIMER'S DISEASE

Edited by Jessica Bryan

Lompico Creek Press • Felton, California

LOMPICO CREEK PRESS
P.O. Box 1403
Felton, California 95018-1403
(831) 335-7696
editor@sasquatch.com
www.loveisageless.com

Love Is Ageless – Stories About Alzheimer's Disease
2nd Edition
© Copyright 2002 by Jessica Bryan

Permissions and credits can be found
on pages 234-244.

Cover Art: Ceramic bas-relief "Frances' Room"
by Gloria Benedetti Seneres
Cover Design: Cheryl Fuller, Proteus Graphics,
Palo Alto, California

ISBN 0-9619311-1-6

Library of Congress Catalog Card Number:
2001 135600

Made in the United States of America

Dedicated to

Gladys and Irma Creveling

Isabel Kennedy

and

William Gonet, who once told me:

"If you're sick, you're sick;

If you're not, get up and dance!"

CONTENTS

EDITOR'S PREFACE

When my mother began to act strangely in the mid-1980s, I had never heard of Alzheimer's disease. She was only in her 60s, and since she had always been a little mentally unbalanced, I just thought she was becoming more so. Like many of us, I managed the best I could, and not always very well.

Towards the end of her life, the term "Alzheimer's disease" became more widely known, but when I looked for information in my local library, I was dismayed to find there were very few books in print on the subject. It was then that I decided to put together this anthology. I envisioned it as a "support group in a book" where each reader could find something reminiscent of their own family situation and thus experience understanding, a feeling of camaraderie, and compassion for themselves and others. I still envision it in this way, and although there is now a plethora of books in print on the subject, I still feel *Love Is Ageless* is unique and valuable reading, both for those with Alzheimer's disease in their families and the general public.

Looking back on my relationship with my mother, I realize that after the anguish, the weeping, the rage, fear, denial, and utter confusion, I am left with simple and almost unbearably sweet memories:

Holding hands with her in the early twilight as we danced to Aretha Franklin on the radio, or laughing over our Christmas dinner of enchiladas at a Mexican restaurant, tomato sauce and cheese smeared all over everything, as if it was my own small child I entertained.

For it was in these few fleeting moments at the end of her life, and the end of our troubled and volatile relationship, that I learned what love is – that simple state of being with another for however brief a time you have together, no matter what the circumstances.

This is what I want you to feel as you read these heartfelt stories and poems, for they are a magnificent

1

testament to families everywhere. They show us over and over again that love is always possible, no matter how difficult our circumstances.

I offer my gratitude to all of the writers who have shared their stories in this book and to Helen Kennedy, Cindy Stevens, Katie Cameron, and Tom Clunie for their ongoing support and encouragement.

Jessica Bryan
Felton, California
June 2002

INTRODUCTION
Victor Molinari, Ph.D.

The psychological consequences of caring for Alzheimer's disease patients have been extensively documented: as many as one-half of the primary caregivers become significantly depressed. A great majority of these caregivers are close relatives, usually spouses or children, who must deal with the loss of their loved ones as they once knew them, as well as face the social isolation engendered by their "36-hour" days.

The stories and poetry in this collection paint a poignant picture of the diverse issues these relatives and caregivers face and the emotional stress they must endure. Although the mood tone varies from the humorous (*My Alzheimer's Percussion Band: unplugged version*) to the resigned (*That's What Its All About*), to the exalted (*Tyrone Street*), they are personal statements of people refusing to abandon their own. As such, they are tributes to the majority of American families who honor their parents. Each is a unique portrayal of a universal caregiving dilemma: given a prior loving relationship, how can one continue to love an increasingly dependent individual who will never again be able to reciprocate.

Walks With My Father is a nostalgic tale of a daughter who goes on a stroll with her demented father and reminisces about the earlier times that generated the tenderness she now expresses with her caregiving.

I know Dr. Alzheimer, written by a physician, shows the pathos that results when medical "science" meets face-to-face with the unknown and indefinite. It powerfully calls into question traditional definitions of love in caregiving situations, when love as an intense personal bond between two equal partners is disbanded and becomes transformed into a banal cliché by the impaired person's insatiable neediness. Love then becomes blindly non-historical and is given freely to anyone who may be fleetingly helpful. *Calle*

3

España, also written by a physician, expresses the terror the author felt as a five-year-old boy when he first encountered a senile neighbor who was "losing her mind." Such an experience is forever implanted in the psyche, and the emotions it generates are reawakened throughout adulthood whenever one attempts to handle "logically" that which defies reason.

In *Details*, a son's disquieting visit to his mother in a nursing home chronicles his efforts at mentally escaping into the mundane aspects of life, although there is no escape from her ongoing life-or-death drama. The "magic pills" he administers like a potion to cure his mother serve his own personal ritual of expiation. Likewise, in *Missing Items* the wife of a memory-impaired husband alternates between acceptance and denial before reaching a compromise with her new bitter reality.

Many of the poems in this collection outline the regressive nature of Alzheimer's disease: how it not only devastates the memory of the victim, but also how it blurs the personal connections between past and present. *Technical Difficulty* traces a mother's regression back through all the stages of her life, until she ends up at "a place only faith can see, the beginning-the end-the starting again." *Spanish Enters The Room, Mother-in-law,* and *After The Visit Of An Elderly Relative* all speak to the tragic-comedic aspects of caregivers wresting dignity from so undignified a condition.

In *Coming Into This World* and *St. Luke's Garden,* we hear directly from two seniors dealing with Alzheimer's. They offer us insight into their situations as if they know they are already in the process of leaving. In *Coming Into This World,* Richard Waller, age 84, tells us, "I haven't overdone or underdone, but I could do it more." While Lillian Waller, age 91, muses, "I came from nowhere and I went to everywhere. No, there's no other place like this."

These glimpses into the lives of a variety of families offer just a sample of the myriad reactions of human beings caught in an intense and unremitting predicament. We are taught to love our elders, yet the effect of Alzheimer's disease on personality and behavior renders the afflicted relative unrecognizable ("...Your deep colors fade to a pastel you never were" – from *The Dance*), thereby placing great strain, even in the best circumstances, on those who try to live up to their duties. When early relationships are less than ideal, ambivalence in caregivers may result, with vacillation between love and resentment ("...You are pressed to my chest, hammered by exactly two tears" – from *The Dance*) overriding the demented person's need for stability.

In *The Nursing Home*, a son visits his mother and muses: "The sons who had been exiled to boarding school by the age of seven had now exiled their own mother." His fear of catching Alzheimer's, and being placed in a nursing home himself, reflects the guilt over the role he played in his mother's fate, and perhaps fear that his own children will treat him likewise. Yet, he still cares about her – family bonds are weakened by past feuds, but not broken.

This disease creates confusion in the caregivers' lives, awakens dormant but powerful memories, necessitates role reversals, and forges coping skills from unused potential. From such crises, personal growth is forced out of psychological complacency as in *Testing Stars* when the author realizes "I am like a new mother, suddenly come to know that what I tend is much more than I had bargained for," or in *Life With Irma* when a daughter observes that she and her mother are "both becoming someone else, but we haven't yet recognized who we are."

The trusted and guilt-ridden son in *Passover* supports his mother in her fight against his father's paranoia, but he too fails. He becomes "the son who does not even know how to ask a question," and he is unable to protect his family from its own private plague.

These caregiving experiences can create wisdom in those who accept the painful side of attachment. In *Dancing In The Wind*, a nurse empathizes with her clients without pity. Her nursing home experiences have allowed her a "skewed perspective like a gift of non-Euclidean sight, so that I become as willing to dip and bend with the motion of a damaged cortex as a tree in wind." But like all the caregivers in these pieces, she heeds the warnings of a senile patient, which could be emblazoned as the caregivers' motto: "Don't stop trying, dear." By our efforts we validate our own humanity, even when a little of theirs has so humanly failed.

5

The Funeral Parlor and *The Old Man's Love* use dying as a metaphor for Alzheimer's disease. Death of the mind and ultimately of the body may yield mixed blessings for the patient and caregiver, as the banter of the children of the deceased in *The Funeral Parlor* makes clear. *The Old Man's Love* reflects the long dormant unrequited love of a dying artist who is finally able to magically unite with his forsaken sweetheart via the altered consciousness of the state of dementia. His family undergoes a parallel process of painful confrontation with his past.

Finally, *The Same Rain* and *Life With Irma* highlight the crises, mixed feelings, and self-discoveries of daughters dealing with eccentric and lovable mothers. In *The Same Rain*, the daughter reluctantly seeks and ultimately finds reconciliation with a long lost but now demented mother. In *Life With Irma*, the author experiences the initial confusion of not knowing what is wrong, governmental bureaucracy that at times sacrifices "common sense" for rigid adherence to guidelines, and the fumbling of a medical establishment that offers more clichés than answers. She experiences the drastic role changes that senility necessitates whereby she becomes "mother" to her mother and finally understands that her brother helped all he could within the parameters of his own relationship with their mother. One does not have to agree with all this daughter's actions or her philosophical bias to appreciate the warmth that flows through the pages, even as her failures as the "perfect child" are clearly evident.

I expect that most family members caring for senile patients will be able to identify with both this increasingly common predicament and the individualized responses of the book's authors. Realizing they do not shoulder their burdens alone, they ultimately may grieve and accept their own personal family tragedy. As the title of the poem *Simply Must* suggests, ultimately we must trust the healing power of love.

THE BLACK HOLE
Bobbi Lurie

Matilda went wild at 65. Legs left unshaven for the first time in 50 years, hair stiff and proud, knotted with forgetting, she'd roam the streets at night. A traveler without design, Matilda was a gardener of sorts, digging up all previous assumptions, scattering the seeds of her memory across the unspoken laws of human society.

Matilda felt remarkably free and lost at the same time. "God has taken me over," she shouted gleefully to her daughter Marianne, one evening after the police found her taking a sponge bath in front of the Johnson's garden sprinklers. Naked, except for her husband Raymond's underwear and his old red and green plaid slippers, the ones she had hated and wanted to throw out before he died, Matilda smiled broadly at the moon, a moon she had never bothered to look at in her younger days.

Perhaps it was Raymond's death last June that set her in motion. After 46 years of bickering and finding fault with one another, his absence left a blank space, a void, a vacuum of sorts. There was nothing to resist or to lean on. Her identity was hard to fathom.

After Raymond died, Matilda could not find any reason to leave her house in the daytime. The bright light of the sun made the world seem both brazenly insignificant and far away. Night, however, resembled the inside of her brain where thoughts would appear in bold clarity against the comforting darkness. She took to sleeping during the day and roaming the streets at night. Although her daughter tried to argue her out of her reclusiveness and begged her to refrain from her night wanderings, Matilda experienced herself as alive and vital in her solitude and confusion. Although she often felt lost, she no longer felt bored. She no longer asked for anything other than what she had.

"You can't keep shutting yourself away from the world, Mom, and you've got to stop leaving the house at night. Please try and pull yourself together," begged Marianne.

"I'm fine. I'm fine," said Matilda. She felt a vague longing to say more but the words wouldn't come.

No longer eligible to depend on the laws of the universe, Matilda gave into the demands of what she called the "black hole." Socks, shoes, checkbooks, and vitamin pills were scooped up into the black hole constantly. Its power to attract all the objects in her possession was uncanny. Spoons, forks, books, and bras all met the same fate. The black hole was her master.

She spent her days looking for the objects she lost. She would look for what was missing and then forget what she was looking for so that she was left only with the hazy sensation that something essential was missing. Most objects could never be found again, except with Marianne's help. Daylight kept Matilda a prisoner. But as the sky changed colors at dusk, Matilda would also change. She stopped searching. She grew more confident, less confused.

The night fell like velvet. Its softness would caress her. All became equal in darkness. Matilda could walk freely down Phillips Street, unnoticed and completely at ease. She could talk as loud as she wanted and hum the newly remembered childhood melodies that had begun to emerge spontaneously from her lips.

Matilda had stopped washing her clothes and then she stopped wearing her clothes. She wore Raymond's clothes now. She wore his underwear and shirts. She put his pants on inside out, tying them at the waist with the remaining portion of the ruptured clothesline. She'd slip her feet into his mildewed slippers, which now exuded a fading but precious perfume, feeling a dim memory of the caress of him and all the spirited anger they had shared. She would walk out into the night feeling the air against her cheeks, feeling herself walking out as Raymond.

When Raymond was alive she had fought against his domination of her. Now she could wear him in leisure. She could feel his presence without being overwhelmed by it. She remembered his body lying dead in the mortuary. He seemed more whole and present than she had ever remembered him being in life. She felt him now to be more

8

a part of her than ever before. He had floated up to become God.

"God save me!" she would cry when confronted with the obstinacy of the black hole, and then she would laugh. God was close to her now. She was wearing God. God was part of her.

Matilda covered a lot of territory on her walks down Phillips Street, but once she started losing her way, wandering across Junction Corner or through the Bounty High School soccer field, making her bed beside the trash cans outside the locker room, both the police and Marianne decided that Matilda's life would have to change.

Marianne looked into her mother's still-beautiful face. Matilda was laughing and screaming at the moon, "God has taken me over! God has taken me over!" All the years she had seen her mother neatly dressed in a shirtwaist dress, high heels, and nylons evaporated before her. Marianne knew she had lost her mother forever. While Matilda laughed, spreading her arms out towards the star-lit sky, Marianne felt abandoned in the starkness of the black night and the isolation of memories.

* * *

Marianne decided the best thing for everyone would be to put Matilda in a nursing home. There was only one nursing home in their small town: The Golden Pavilion.

The Golden Pavilion. Its name held out some sort of promise. An awkward parody of Japanese grace and design, it was really a bold example of American kitsch. Once Marianne passed through the pillars in the entryway, once the memory of Japanese lanterns left one's range of vision, once the scent of lilacs left the nostrils, all attempts at evoking Japan were gone. Even as one entered the darkened entryway, the odor of urine and ammonia overwhelmed all the other senses.

Matilda had looked at the word "Golden" after Marianne shut the door behind her. She held onto that word for a longer moment than was usually possible. Golden. Golden. Golden years. Golden money. Golden proof of life's insubstantiality. A change had happened, a lifting from the earth. Matilda held Marianne's hand as she walked through the hall.

9

For Marianne, no name, no smell, no dark hallways could hide the shock of the people who lived in the Golden Pavilion. Not all the residents were old, but they all seemed finished with this world. Sounds of moaning could be heard. Many of those who could not walk were tied in wheelchairs, some with their heads down, some with drool streaming from mouths that once demanded attention, once offered common sense or humor or anger or fear or doubt. They sat in the main room past the darkened entryway. They sat staring into or past or through or away from the giant television screen that stood in the middle of the room and served as its centerpiece. Sounds and images poured out from the giant screen with promises of brighter teeth, younger skin, and better days.

Marianne introduced Matilda to a fat woman who met them as they walked in the door. She smiled broadly at Matilda, but Matilda looked past her into the television set where a fast red car was zooming over hills to a café next to the ocean. A woman with long black hair ran across acres of manicured green grass. She jumped into a tall man's arms. They kissed, drank wine, and started to dance.

"My name is Jenny," the fat woman said. There was food between her teeth and her eyes looked angry. "Let me show you to your room"

Matilda continued to hold onto Marianne's hand. She squeezed it tight, feeling as if her daughter were slipping away. Matilda imagined herself floating as they walked down the darkened hallways, passing people whose emptiness reflected something familiar and easy. She could sense that they too had opened themselves into the arms of God.

Matilda's room was very small and narrow. Its only furnishings were a single bed' and a freestanding metal closet. "Well, Mom," said Marianne, suddenly cheerful, "this should make things less confusing for you." Then Marianne and the fat woman talked about her symptoms and odd tendencies as she walked over to the window and looked outside to where the word "GOLDEN" stood against the dark gray sky.

After Marianne and the fat woman left, Matilda sat on the edge of her bed feeling no different than she ever had before. She opened the suitcase Marianne had packed for her. None of Raymond's clothes were to be found. Matilda unpacked and repacked the suitcase, looking for anything that might have belonged to him. She no longer cared what the black hole took as long as it was not something of Raymond's.

She unpacked and re-packed, folded and unfolded and refolded the clothes from the suitcase, feeling lost and alone. She stacked the clothes in piles and put them in the bottom of the closet, and then she took them out and spread them across the bed. She took off the dress Marianne had insisted she wear that morning. She tried on sweaters and shoes, but nothing seemed to fit. She took off everything but Raymond's jockey shorts, which she had managed to wear beneath her dress that morning without Marianne's interference. She suddenly felt very tired. She lay down on the narrow bed and slept until she was woken.

A young man, whose skin still smelled of childhood, woke her. He dressed her carefully, choosing from among the clothes strewn across the bed. Then he gently took her arm and walked her to a large, windowless room; he offered her a seat at a table in the back next to the wall.

Matilda sat and watched as people were brought into the dining room. An old man was wheeled in beside her. He did not speak. He wore a flannel shirt just like Raymond's. It was gray and white plaid with black buttons down the front. The man looked distant and sad. Matilda reached out for his hand and squeezed it hard. She leaned towards him slowly and whispered in his ear, "I've always loved you. I've always loved you. I've always loved you." The old man dropped his head into his hands and started to weep. He wept and wept. Then he turned to Matilda, looked her squarely in the face, and smiled as if life had finally given him everything it once promised.

TECHNICAL DIFFICULTY
Ronnie R. Brown

Like in a thirties movie –
the kind her dates had taken her to see,
the kind we'd watched together
on t.v. – time
was moving rapidly. The hands
of the clock had started to spin,
the pages of the calendar to fly.
But the whole scene was running
in reverse,
a technical difficulty, and I
could only watch, observe
as she re-played her life

moved from mother,
wife, back
to the teenager fate
had not allowed her to be.
Sixty-three and there she stood:
pinafored, bobby-soxed, fingering
gray-streaked pigtails, curling
her upper lip as she
defied authority. Passionate, alive
her hips re-claimed their girlish sway
as she sauntered back,
back, day by day, through all the stages
of a girl. Skipping, singing back
to a toddler of two or three.

Back
to accidents and toys;
a frightened little girl
walking awkwardly. Back
to the confines of a sided bed,
to infancy, to being bathed, clothed,

changed. Back to a newborn,
responding to a smile but not a name.
Back to tears, wonder, fear
in wide unknowing eyes.

Back until
standing by her bed
I saw her fetus-like: tiny
knees pressed to a tiny chest. Arms
circling in. Saw and wondered
if, how, when
that body had held me. I looked
at that unformed face and questioned
if I'd ever really held a place
in her life.

But questions
did not slow her pace. She moved on,
back, unceasingly. Back until she,
the calendar, the clock were all renewed.
Time drew her back till new was old,
old new...back, back, back,
to a place which only faith can see,
the beginning – the end – the starting
again.

WALKS WITH MY FATHER
Elisavietta Ritchie

"Daddy, let's take a walk."

It's a June day in Virginia. He nods, puts his hands on the arms of his wheelchair, whispers something that makes little sense. I try to help him up, but he is too heavy, and limp.

"Come for a walk, and then – I've brought you a surprise."

The breeze billows white curtains into the room.

Shivering, he murmurs something about blizzards. Then slightly more audibly, "It's cold and I'm tired. Can't we go home now?"

Suddenly we're far beyond Lake Shore Drive, in a part of the waterfront I've never seen before. December, Chicago, I'm five, and cold. One mitten's lost. My feet are tired. His legs are longer and he walks too quickly through yellowing snow, gritty slush, towards buildings like airplane hangers with cavernous, menacing mouths.

He begins to tell me about ships and cargoes.

Usually I love to listen to his stories; he knows about everything in the world, but I've had enough walking. "I want to go home."

"Just as far as that warehouse." He strides on. "Right foot, left foot, you'll see – we could hike around the whole of Lake Michigan. Come on, hold my hand – Forward <u>March</u>!"

"I don't want to hike around Lake Michigan."

But we reach the warehouse – *shed*, he calls it, though it is 100 times bigger than any shed in anyone's back yard. By the pier beyond are big boats – tugs and freighters and tankers and tramps. Huge anchors. I keep hoping someone will drop them with a splash into the water. But the ships are docked with thick hawsers, nooses to choke the pilings. Crates taller than my father sit on the wharves. The funnels and cranes are silent: Sunday, and no one is working.

Suddenly the nearest freighter bellows from her funnel and I jump. From excitement, I insist, not fear.

This is the most exciting place I have ever been. I could walk along here forever, or at least until I find out how to get aboard one of the boats.

Smaller sheds now, smaller boats, a green diner. Odor of fish, and smoke. We enter a shack. Barrels of brine, string bags of clams, crates of fish laid out on ice, their eyes terribly wide.

"Daddy, look at that snake!"

"No, that's an eel," he says. "We'll take it home for supper."

"I certainly won't eat that!"

As we walk back, smelly package in hand, he tells me about migrations of eels to the Sargasso Sea; how eels come down the Damaltian rivers and swim across the Mediterranean, and then the whole Atlantic, and eels come from the rivers of North America too. They spawn in the warm Sargasso Sea – though I'm not quite sure what that means. Then the baby elvers swim back to the native rivers of their parent eels. My father explains that spawn is a nicer word for something my grandmothers say people aren't supposed to discuss. But about eels, that's okay.

"Someday I will take one of these big ships. No," I correct myself, "a real sailing ship, and I'll steer it to the Sargasso Sea."

He warns me that if I sail into the Sargasso Sea, the rudder or the propeller screw might get stuck in seines of floating algae, and I'd never get home again.

Home is already far, Lake Michigan is too large, and although he sings old army marching songs to urge me to pick up my steps, toward the end of the journey he lets me ride home on his shoulders.

Back inside the apartment at last, he unwraps the eel, opens his Swiss Army penknife (though he could have used the big kitchen knife) and slices carefully.

"I won't eat it," I say firmly.

"Try one bite, just for me."

"I won't like it."

While he hangs up our coats, finally I test one crumb. Awfully smelly, smoky, and salty.

He goes into the kitchen to heat milk for my cocoa and tea for himself in the samovar from Tula. I test one more sliver. Then another. When he returns with the steaming cups, the whole eel is gone.

Because it is Sunday and I am five, he forgives me.

* * *

Later I am seven, or twelve, or fifteen. We are walking along the canal, or a river, or best of all, a beach. No eels now, but we see frogs and ducks, water snakes and minnows. He tells me about everything in the world. We talk about fishing.

Sometimes at the ocean we cast from a rock or pier or the beach, though it is always the wrong bait or the wrong tide. We drop hand-lines over the side of somebody's boat. On rare occasions, we catch a keeper. Then he takes out his Swiss Army knife and teaches me to clean and fillet the fish. His hair sparkles with scattered fish scales and so does mine. Often we spread a picnic: black bread, smelly cheese, and a tin of sardines. Now I eat only my share.

At nineteen, during a college vacation, I fly out to join my parents in Japan. My father and I climb Mount Fuji. High above the Pacific, and hours up the cindery slope with only dried eel, seaweed crackers, cold rice wrapped in the skin of an eel. He reaches the peak first.

Through the years we hike along a beach in Cyprus, beside a river in Lebanon, the Seine, Alpine streams, and picnic by various other waters and weathers. We overtake one another. Even among my contemporaries, I've never known anyone with such energy.

* * *

Today in the nursing home in Virginia I beg him, "Please Daddy, you need to exercise. Just a little walk."

He can't get out of his chair, because I've forgotten to untie the straps of the "posey" that restrains him. If he gets up on his own, he is likely to topple over. I crouch to lift his feet from the foot petals and fold up the metal pieces, which too often bruise his paper-thin skin.

"Come, now you can stand, and we'll take a short walk."

He struggles, but cannot move. I place his hands on the rubberized handholds of the metal walker. "Hold tightly and you can pull yourself up."

16

He grips the walker and struggles forward. Gradually I lift and push and pull him to his feet. Now he is standing, unsteadily, but then appears to gain his balance.

"See – you made it! Hold my arm – forward, march! First your right foot – now your left."

He shuffles a couple of steps along the hall, but then the rubber caps on the tips of the walker catch on the linoleum and he tilts and plunges forward. I pull him back and steady the walker. He pauses for several minutes, just standing there. I realize he has forgotten what to do next.

"Just move the walker a bit – <u>forward</u>, Daddy – then move your feet – <u>forward</u>."

He is impatient with the walker and so am I. We make it to the dining room. I help him into his chair and hand him a spoon. It slips from his fingers. Pureed tuna is heaped on a plastic plate. I encourage him to eat, sing him old songs, tell stories, but he does not eat.

When I lift a spoonful of the gray fishy stuff to his mouth, he says politely, "I don't care for any."

Nor would I.

Then I take the small, smelly package wrapped in glazed ivory paper from a plastic bag. He loves presents, and reaches forward with awkward fingers to try and open it. The smell fills the room.

"Look, Daddy, they've been out of it for months, but this morning at a fishmonger's near the Potomac, I found some smoked eel."

We unwrap it together and I take out his Swiss Army knife my stepmother gave me for "safekeeping" and slice the silvery flesh. My father beams, picks it up with steady fingers and, slice by slice, eats the whole piece.

STILL HERE
Nancy Watts

When the autumn winds shake the
core of your foundation, it will not be
my hand that fells you to the ground.

I will not leave you as underbrush,
to become brittle and burn with
summer's first crack of lightning.

Instead, I will scoop in my arms
the part of you that can
warm me on cold winter nights.

Looking forward to spring and the
greener, richer version of that which,
like the great redwood, only grows
more precious and rare with age.

I KNOW, DR. ALZHEIMER
Andrew N. Wilner, M.D., FACP

"I love you," he whispered.

Who could not be touched, I thought, as I waited for my new patient to enter the room. His soft words barely carried to my chair by his bed. This old man, stooped and shuffling entered his hospital room reluctantly. He clung to his wife in fear as she accompanied him to the tidy hospital bed. Watching his stiff, slow movements, I thought an eternity would pass before I could begin the interview.

"He didn't want to come today," the old woman told me. "But I had to bring him, you know, he just can't seem to manage at home. It's all I can do to dress him and feed him and look after him. He wanders around at all hours of the night, tells me he's heard burglars, and he won't sleep. Sometimes well, sometimes at night he can't find the bathroom."

She admitted this last piece of information with a tired voice that betrayed her frustration and shame. Now that they lived alone, and her husband could not go out, she was the only witness to his mental and physical deterioration. Only she could tell me what had happened and when.

"I brought you his medicines, doctor. I can never remember their names."

She pulled from her worn purse a small brown paper bag. I thought of the little bags an old man at the corner store used to put penny candy in twenty years ago. The storekeeper had long since gone and now the bags were plastic.

"This one is for his heart, once a day, this one for his blood pressure, twice a day, this white one for his arthritis, four times a day, and this one, well, I don't remember what it's for doctor; he just started it a few weeks ago."

She held out the large blue pill to me. The saucer shaped medicine quivered in her palm with the fine tremor of her hand. I could see she was painfully embarrassed at having forgotten the purpose of the medication. Her failure reminded her of her husband's failure to improve. She could not, their doctor could not, and the expensive medicine whose name eluded her could not help him. Even fifty years of love had not prevented this.

"Is it for diabetes?" I asked. I recognized the pill and had been told of this new problem by his family doctor over the phone.

"Yes, yes, oh yes," she exclaimed. "That's it."

"Thank you," I replied. "I'm glad you brought these medications with you. Most people are not so thoughtful."

She sighed. The muscles of her back, which had been so tense, relaxed, and her stout frame eased into the hospital chair. She could rest a bit, now that she had discharged this one last responsibility.

"Is there anything your husband complains of?" I asked.

She turned and looked at him. He stared straight ahead, his cloudy blue eyes looking at me without a flicker of emotion. Then he turned to look at her. I saw on his profile a stubble of white beard clinging to his chin. It must have been too difficult for the old woman to shave for fear of cutting him.

His long nose was handsome and gave him a serious air. I could see by his broad shoulders that once he must have been a strong man. Perhaps he had even carried her over the threshold.

"I love you," he said.

She smiled and kissed him, hugged him and looked into his eyes. "I love you too, dear. I know I brought you to the hospital and you didn't want to come, but the doctor's here and he seems to be a nice young man, don't you think? He's here to help you. We're all here to help you."

She turned her eyes from the man's stoic face and looked to me for confirmation.

"Yes, I'm here to help you," I assured her. "That's my job." I smiled at her.

She wanted to trust me, but she could not. How many of her friends had gone to the hospital and never returned? How many of his? Just from the statistics of it, she knew he might never come home again. And it was she who brought him here, into the hands of strangers, a land of high technology, long incomprehensible words, and death.

But it was also the place of miracles. This she had heard on the radio and seen on TV. She had read about them in the newspaper, miracles at this very hospital. And yet, so many of their friends had come here and not returned.

Again she was stiff in her chair. "What are you going to do?" she queried.

"I don't know yet," I told her honestly. "I need to talk to your husband and examine him, and then I think I'll know a great deal more. Why don't you leave us alone for about thirty minutes, and then we can talk about what I've found and what we can do."

She looked at me, studying my face for any trace of complicity. If she could not trust fate, which had denied her husband's health, how could she trust this doctor she had never seen before, and such a young one at that?

"I assure you he'll be fine with me. By the way, in six months I'll have my own private practice. I have seen many cases like this one. In any event, I will discuss your husband's problems with the senior staff and he will also be seen by a neurologist." I hoped that my assurances would convince her to leave us so I could get on with my work. This man was not the only one I had to see this afternoon, and time was moving on.

"Yes, all right," she said. She looked again at her husband and his blue eyes turned to her. Then his craggy jaw dropped slowly and I heard the three words, "I love you."

"Oh yes, dear, I love you too!" she said, grabbing his crooked hands and holding them together in hers as if to squeeze her warmth and strength into them.

Slowly, he turned away from her to look at me. The old woman took this as a sign and put his two hands quietly into his lap. She was so anxious, that had I closed the window to shut out the din of the city traffic, I'm sure I could have heard her heart pounding against her ribs. A trapped bird could not have felt more fearful, more desperate.

Then with one more look at me and another at him, she flew from the room. I was amazed to see this large woman move so quickly, and I was relieved. Finally, I could get down to business. This man had heart disease, severe degenerative joint disease, and new onset diabetes. He had become confused over the past few months, more so in the past few days. These details I had learned from the family physician.

Now I could get to his story. Then I wanted to proceed with the entire mental status exam. I wanted to make my own assessment of what was wrong and what could be done.

I was encouraged by the interaction I had witnessed between my patient and his wife. This strong emotional bond suggested that his mind was still intact. Perhaps his confusion was due to some metabolic imbalance, a recent infection, or perhaps a side effect from his medications. Any of these problems could be quickly remedied.

Yet, the story I had heard could just as easily represent that of a dementia, usually irreversible and terminal. Only a few cases ever improved.

But I had my hopes and pressed on. I addressed the man, looking carefully into his clouded eyes.

"So, tell me sir, how have you been feeling?"

"I love you," he said.

COMING INTO THIS WORLD
Richard T. Waller, Age 84

In coming into this world you have things.
The good part was I had to show
I appreciated; the trouble is I never think.
I quickly wisk it off.
Some of us should be given a time
to sift down and answer in our own words
what was good and what was not.
There is some connection.
Everyone has a little piece.
People have different amounts.
Richness of the tough,
I haven't overdone or underdone but
I could do it more.
It's not a crumbling thing.
A person can hurt himself.
He's bound to take over.

* * *

I've been putting things away
the things you accumulate
without really thinking what there is,
many things...so many...not one.
In coming into this world
you have things.
One thing...I had too much.
I throw away a lot.
But that doesn't mean you.
I wouldn't do that.
Would you write me a letter?

MY ALZHEIMER'S PERCUSSION BAND – Unplugged Version
Stephen J. Lyons

An incident, ugly in nature if only because eighty-year-old women are not graceful at this sort of display, occurred recently at the local nursing home's Alzheimer's unit, and I am partially to blame. Let's call the instigator "Dotty," to protect her guilt. She was the one who clapped (as hard as her small hands could manage) the two wooden blocks she uses as percussion instruments directly in the right ear of a woman we shall call "Jean" (to protect her innocence). If Dotty, who is fragile in stature but sturdy of wit, had simply demonstrated the blocks to Jean instead of playing them like orchestra cymbals, none of this would have happened. Instead, Dotty was emphatically punctuating a song I had just finished singing.

Every Wednesday I gather my Alzheimer's Percussion Band for an hour of song. The first task is to pass out instruments. Spoons require the most dexterity, so hardly anyone ever chooses them. More popular, and easier to play, are the pear-shaped castanets with pastel designs of parrots and sombreros painted on the sides that create an idea of Mexico. Pairs of slim pine sticks are distributed with the break-even chance that whoever takes them will be able to click them together. The remaining bracelets of bells end up on the slim wrists of women like Betty Lou, who cannot handle the bells and, at the same time, sing softly to her stuffed dog.

This dog and assorted baby dolls are the source of additional incidents (such as theft) by one ambulatory woman Amy, who is known to boldly shuffle up to Betty Lou (and other women confined to wheelchairs) and tug the stuffed animal or coveted doll from her arms. Then Amy steals down the hallway to her room (carefully avoiding the nurses and aides), where she slams the door. Other acts of geriatric mischief abound, but back to Dotty.

If you recall the quick spiritual *Down by the Riverside*, you will remember that at the end of each phrase of the verses there is a musical opportunity to add a two-beat bit of rhythm. "Gonna lay down my sword and shield," Bam! Bam! "Down by the Riverside," Bam! Bam! "Down by the Riverside," Bam! Bam! The guitar player (if willing and coordinated) will slap the front of the guitar or mute the strings with his palm, emphasizing the full chord. Dotty is the only resident that can play her wooden blocks in time to my strumming, and she shows her enthusiasm by ending our entire fifteen-song repertoire with two loud bangs, even the quiet ballad *Michael Row Your Boat Ashore.*

Not content to simply let the song end, so we could move on to *Polly Wolly Doodle All Day*, Dotty gave Jean what can be aptly called "a wake-up call." Up to that morning's turn for the worst, Jean had not been interested in any of the music, not even in *Take Me Out to the Ballgame*, so popular among the residents that we sing it twice: at the beginning and at the end of our song hour. Jean's disapproving scowl is that of someone who suspects I am trying to pull a fast one over on her or, worse, that I am what in this small rural community might be known as a *wisenheimer*, a smart aleck often from an urban area. After a pair of ear-shattering bangs, Jean slowly turned to Dotty and smacked her twice on the upper arm before Pauline, the activities director, came to sooth over the incident. The next week Dotty and Jean were not sitting side-by-side, but Dotty still did wield the blocks.

One hundred-year-old Pearl Engel sits to my left in a bright plum-colored sweater and handles the castanets. She always has a winning attitude. "Doesn't her hair look beautiful?" she comments when Marythea returns from the nursing home salon with her new perm. "That was so beautiful," after hearing my solo of Doc Watson's *Windy and Warm.* Midway through the weekly practice, I always play a solo, to give the residents a break and to show off my finger-picking skills, which, I strongly believe, are somewhere in the intermediate to advanced stage. This nursing home gig, as rewarding as it might be, is not what I had in mind when I first picked up the guitar at the age of ten. I imagined playing to a packed house at Chicago's Earl of Old Town pub, joined during my set by John Prine, Tom

Rush, or the late Steve Goodman, my folk heroes. Then Carnegie Hall and a four-disc contract.

But unlike those other imagined venues, this real one grants an absence of stage fright, which, I am certain, has kept me from larger, more appreciative audiences. Even in the casual company of friends, I can never master the tricky picking pattern required in *I Am a Pilgrim*, or the complicated jazz arrangement of *Somewhere Over the Rainbow* as effortlessly as I do for my seniors. If I flub a transition no one notices. My rather limited range of vocals is politely overlooked. When the pesky "B" string goes out of tune there is not one wince. In the Alzheimer's unit, all is forgiven if not instantly forgotten. The other day Dora (age ninety) said she wanted me to meet her father. "You would like him." An aide passing by whispered to me, "If her father shows up, I'm outta here."

When I walk into the day room of this county nursing home at ten o'clock each Wednesday morning, I see a semi-circle of mostly women in wheelchairs in various stages of chatter, sleep, and laughter. A notice board announces the activities of the day: kickball (played from a sitting position), Yahtzee, sensory exercise, church service, reading group, and quilting. The board also states the date, the weather (very cold), and the next holiday (Valentine's Day). Staff and volunteers provide alternatives to my song sessions. "Does anyone want to go to Mass today?" "Time to have your hair done." We have no official groupies as such, but occasionally family members will join band members for the musical sessions. Lyle, for instance, paces next to his wife, Alma, who never opens her eyes. Lyle appears uncomfortable with my song selections, although he will laugh at my jokes: "Here's a little number by George Gershwin and his lovely wife, Ira."

One day as I was packing up my music stand, Lyle beckoned me into his wife's room. He whispered, "This is what these people are used to singing," and, with all the solemnity of passing an heirloom fiddle, he placed in my palm a tattered songbook, *The One Hundred and One Best Songs*, revised 48th edition published by The Cable Company in 1948. I knew hardly any of the songs that included, *March of the Men of Harlech* (the Welsh national melody), *Bridal Chorus from 'Loengrin,' We are Little Soldier*

26

Men, The Harp that Once Through Tara's Halls, and Stephen C. Foster's, *Massa's in de Cold, Cold Ground.*

Foster's composition was of particular interest to me, but after studying the lyrics I decided against the song.

> Massa makes de darkies love him,
> Cayse he was so kind;
> Now dey sadly weep above him,
> Mourning cayse he leave dem behind....

As band director I have to be careful. I took a chance on *My Bonny Lies Over the Ocean,* praying that no one in the room was related to a Bonny. We sing *Bonny* a cappella. I tap out the time on my guitar's sound box and Dotty, of course, adds the ending.

> Last night as I lay on my pillow,
> Last night as I lay on my bed.
> Last night as I lay on my pillow,
> I dream'd that my Bonnie was dead.

Nor will I sing Hank Williams' *I'm So Lonesome I Could Cry,* even though my wife loves my arrangement: a descending run I pick on the high "E" string with my ring finger while maintaining a strong alternating bass with my thumb.

> Did you ever see a night so long,
> When time goes crawling by?
> The moon just went behind a cloud,
> I'm so lonesome I could cry.

Hymns are off-limits too, because Pauline says, "Hymns make the residents sad. They remind them of funerals." Still, I sometimes slip into *I'll Fly Away,* an uplifting church sing-a-long about the joyful anticipation of going to heaven. It's a song that pleads for a tambourine, rhythmic clapping, and a trembling trip to the altar, but with the exception of Michael (one of the few men and, therefore, greatly appreciated by the ladies), who raises his hand as if hailing a taxi, there is only the stray offbeat rattle.

27

Just a few more weary days and then,
I'll fly away
To a land where joys shall never end,
I'll fly away.

Dotty also plays a key role on Cole Porter's *Don't Fence Me In.* "OK," I'll say, looking in her direction, "I need the horse sounds, that clippety-clop sound." She knows what I want, but it takes until the chorus to get the blocks working just right. "Just turn me loose and let me straddle my old saddle underneath the western skies." At this point in the melody, Porter wants us to imagine the slow gait of a pinto horse, the up-and-down motion of a rider. As she sits and works the blocks, Dotty trots her feet in perfect time to the melody. "On my kioose, let me wander over yonder 'till I see the mountain rise." (The same horse riding sound can just as easily be made without an instrument. Fix your mouth into a giant "O." Keep it slightly open and cluck your tongue. Control the volume by adjusting the size of the "O.")

With the impetus of our modest musical progress urging our ambitions forward, a Christmas concert was planned. We would entertain relatives with the best of our Wednesday sessions. This was my idea and mine alone. I pictured the surprise and pride in the faces of sons and daughters as they watched their parents sing and beat out a percussive rhapsody to *Bicycle Built for Two, You Are My Sunshine,* and *Home On the Range.* (We would give firm directions to Dotty before the concert and probably skip *Down by the Riverside,* just to be on the safe side.) I could also unveil a snappy version of *Bye Bye Blackbird* that I just learned off a Chet Atkins instructional video. Maybe I would even dust off *The Rights of Man* in dropped-D tuning. Pauline, perhaps not fully appreciating the band's progress, wanted a more traditional Christmas party, where I was to play carols that everyone, including residents and families, could sing. She even offered money, which eased my disappointment considerably. "Maybe you can have your concert in the spring during the wiener roast," she suggested.

Perhaps we weren't as far along as I thought. After all, attendance (not mandatory) was dwindling, and Michael

28

was creating a bit of a distraction. Gertie, a woman I have not mentioned thus far, had taken a shine to him. One sunny fall day, during the singing of *She'll be Coming Around the Mountain*, I saw Gertie walk up to Michael, take his hand, and declare her devotion. Michael, in turn, placed Gertie's hand on his lap and declared his intention. Gertie sternly rebuffed him, and then she went outside, picked some late blooming asters, and presented them to him to show there were no bad feelings.

I am happy to report that the Christmas party was a success. A tenor in a local barbershop quartet covered the vocals, leaving me free to roam the neck of my guitar for some fancy holiday picking. On *Silent Night*, I didn't disappoint. Although nervous before all the guests, who perhaps would not be so quick to forgive a botched note, I managed to execute plenty of exciting flourishes. During the last verse, I looked out at the band members sitting with their families. Everyone was on their best behavior. All was calm. Dotty had her hands in her lap. Amy held a new baby doll – this one a gift from her daughter. Jean might have been smiling. Pearl Engel thought the entire event was "beautiful, just beautiful." I agreed with her, because when I looked over at the usual group of sleeping women slumped in their wheelchairs, every one of them, including Lyle's Alma, were tapping their feet in time with the music. All was bright. Our prospects for the upcoming spring concert had just improved. The possibilities, I now realized, were endless. I was already planning my solo: *What A Wonderful World*, on slide guitar.

TESTING STARS
Jan Bailey

Sometimes you just go off in the car,
I don't know where, and your reasons
are as vaporous as the evening air
you disappear into. I used to think

perhaps you drove around testing stars,
to see how far you could get
beyond the city limits before you were
really lost. Once, I found you in a field

we used to hunt, sitting on a skinned face
of rock, your face cocked to the moon,
unfurrowed, alabaster where the light hit it.

Now when you sleep, a voice so much like
yours, but not you, screams out in a darkness
I can only suppose, like the moon's other
side.

I think it is a terrible fate to listen
with the heart. I am like a new mother,
suddenly come to know that what I tend
is much more than I had bargained for.

Outside a gray sky filters through the
winter trees, the dog scratches at the door,
birds continue at the feeder, all things set to
motion beneath a fading moon.

TYRONE STREET
Dennis Vannatta

Suddenly it came to him, the name of the place – Doyle's Steak House. And with the name came the odor not only of steak, but bacon frying and scrambled eggs, and the cool, lulling murmur of ocean tides. Why? He didn't know. But the name, Doyle's Steak House, yes, he was certain of that. Sitting on the edge of his bed, he raised his hand to shade his eyes from the sun's glare, glinting off the plate-glass window. He squinted to see in, remember.

There was something about the window itself that was important, something beyond the name of the restaurant painted in simple block letters arching across the top of the glass. He could see it so clearly now: he could almost touch it. They would walk down the street, he and Madge, and they'd look at the window, or into the window, and then they'd go into the restaurant and eat or they'd turn around and walk away. What was it they saw? Perhaps one of those signs with *Closed* on one side and *Open* on the other, or maybe a notice advertising the special of the day. He stared hard at the window, trying to see either of those signs hanging there, but it was no good.

It had been 1927 or 1928, he thought. From the intensity of the light shining off the glass, he guessed it was summer, but they weren't hot, he and Madge. No, they were cool, *deliciously* cool. Why were they so cool in the bright summer sun? It was important for him to know, but he would return to that later. One thing at a time.

1927? 1928? They were living in an apartment. They were just married and living in a second-floor apartment reached by a long flight of stairs attached to the outside of the house. He could see the chipped gray paint of the steps. They would leave the apartment and descend past the flat roof of the porch jutting off the back of the house. He could smell the tar and feel the heat rising from the roof

31

as they paused and he pulled her to him and pushed his face into the hollow of her neck.

They were hot, sweaty. But later, in front of Doyle's Steak House, they were so cool. What had happened in between? He closed his eyes and rubbed his temples, but he couldn't bring it back.

There was so much he wanted to bring back. What street had the apartment and steak house been on? The same street, he sensed, but he wasn't certain. In 1927 he could have told you the name of the street without even thinking about it. But now....

He shrugged. There would be time to work on the name of the street, why they were hot and then cool, what was on the window or behind it, all the other questions. He even managed a smile – and why not? Hadn't he already reclaimed the apartment, the restaurant, the wooden stairs, the hot tar of the roof, the odor, the taste of Madge's neck – damp and salty?

And today he could add the name of the restaurant: Doyle's Steak House. He could see it right there in front of him, as close as the wall of his bedroom, those white block letters rising and falling in an arc on the glass, the slatted blinds behind.

The blinds! That's what they looked for. If the blinds were raised, they could see inside, and if the crowd was small, there would be no waiting. If the blinds were lowered and closed, there would be customers waiting for a table. A trick of old Sandy Doyle's to get you inside, obviously, but he and Madge had figured it out. If the blinds were closed, they'd turn around and walk away. Did he really think his little trick would fool anybody?

He looked at Sandy's round, bewhiskered leprechaun face smiling behind the cash register.

* * *

"Dad, was that you I heard laughing?"

A woman was standing in the doorway of his bedroom. She had a look on her face caught between worry and amusement. He nodded.

"Oh, and just what was so funny?" she asked, smiling.

He didn't answer. He looked away and then turned back, canted his head left and looked at her with his good eye. She was a tall woman, big-boned and strong looking, but care lines spread from the corners of her mouth and eyes. Her neck was wrinkled and her hair was graying. He stared and stared, but then turned away, raised a hand to his eyes. He should know her name, but no, it was no good, no use. He had lost it.

The woman sat down on the bed beside him, put her arm around his shoulders, and gave him a squeeze.

"Don't be sad," she said. It hurts me so to see you sad. Tell me what's the matter."

But he said nothing. Her arm was heavy across his shoulders. He hardly felt strong enough to sit up with her arm there. He tried to sneak another look at her, but she was sitting too close and he couldn't focus on her face.

"Don't you know me, Dad? Don't you know who I am?" the woman asked, a slight quaver in her voice.

"Dad," she called him.

"I'm your dad," he said.

She gave him another squeeze.

"Yes, old fox, yes. But what's my name?"

He stared at the wall. He would like to raise his hand to rub his temples, but he was too weak. If the woman would only remove her arm, he'd lie back on the bed.

"Have you forgotten my name, Dad?"

Yes, he had lost her name. But had it happened yesterday? Or a week ago? Or just now?

The losses, which were coming faster and faster now, used to frighten him, but no longer, for think of what he had received in return. Doyle's Steak House! Where the juices would gather reddish-brown around the tines of his fork as he pierced the steak's tender flesh. The baked potatoes, steam rising around the dollops of golden butter, were big as cantaloupes. The salads were fresh and crisp and cold.

"Poor Dad, poor Dad," the woman murmured, laying her head on his shoulder.

He smiled, his mouth watering.

* * *

33

Oh, it was coming, it was on its way, almost here now, he could almost reach out and...yes! There it was.

Sandy Doyle sat behind a cash register that was almost as big as he was. The table on which the cash register squatted was pushed up against the wall on the left. It was a small place, no more than seven or eight tables. Yes, eight, he could see each one clearly now. The blinds were raised; the room was flooded with sunlight; only two or three (yes, three) of the tables were occupied.

He and Madge ordered the same thing every time, the steak dinner – New York strip, baked potato, salad, all for 65 cents. He shook his head and chuckled. 65 cents! "1927, remember," he said to the wall.

And a beer, too. Mustn't forget that. Pony beer, wasn't that it? No, P.O.N.Y. beer. He could see it stenciled on the wooden barrels. Port of New York. He could feel the weight of the cold, beaded bucket and the wire handle cutting across his fingers as he walked. He could hear his father hollering to him from the next room: "Hey, boy, go get me a bucket of pony."

But wait. That was earlier, much earlier, long before Madge. A good memory, one he'd return to, but in its own time.

Not beer, but iced tea in big cold schooners, like beer mugs – that'd been the reason for the confusion. A steak, baked potato, salad, and all the iced tea you could drink for 65 cents.

Oh, he could taste that steak, bleeding pink in the middle but with a pungent, almost blackened outside. He could taste the skin of the potato, jeweled with crystals of baked-on salt, taste the scrambled eggs, a steaming yellow heap on his plate, the bacon crisp as....

Eggs? Bacon? Where did they come from? When he was a boy, maybe, back there with the P.O.N.Y. beer? No, that didn't feel right. The bacon and eggs weren't in Doyle's Steak House, but nearby. He was sure of it.

He watched Madge and himself back out of Doyle's, like a movie reel in reverse, back down the street (what was the name of it?), and then...he lost them.

He searched and searched, then found them again, found them back at the apartment. He was sitting at the table wolfing down those bacon and eggs. God, they tasted wonderful! But he ate quickly, too quickly almost. What was the rush? Why were they in a hurry to get to Doyle's to eat a steak dinner right after all the bacon and eggs?

No, the sun had been high in the sky, bright and hot outside Doyle's (even though he and Madge were deliciously cool), but here the light was more diffuse and pearly, slanting through the window over Madge's shoulder. It must be morning.

Was that really how he had started his mornings back in 1927? No, impossible. They had been poor then. Their "apartment" was no more than a single, fairly large room, with a common bathroom shared with the Finkels. Half the room was taken up by the bed. In the other half was the little table and two chairs, a floor lamp with a homely plaid shade, and two used dressers, one with a mirror where Madge sat brushing out her long red hair each night and one that served as a pantry – their few pots and pans in the bottom drawer and tins of food, sugar, flour, and coffee in the top drawers. Resting on this dresser were two hot plates, one for eggs, one for bacon. But not bacon and eggs every morning – only special occasions, no doubt. Maybe on Saturday or Sunday. Oh, they were good, but he ate hurriedly, as if he couldn't wait to get through with them.

* * *

He frowned at his plate. Something was wrong, but what? He was ready to eat, but he couldn't because of the thing that was wrong.

He had lost something else; he knew that. If he could find the word for it, everything would be all right. Then he would just go right ahead and eat.

He realized that the woman across the table was watching him. He stirred uneasily in his chair.

"Why aren't you eating, Dad? Is something wrong with the food?"

He made vague, hesitant movements over the plate and grunted. Then the woman put something in his hand.

"Fork," of course. That was it. He smiled and turned it this way and that so the tines sparkled and gleamed under the ceiling light. Then his smile faded. "Fork," yes, but what did you do with it, what was it for?

35

Suddenly it was so heavy in his hands; he was so weak. Carefully, with both hands he lowered it to the table. He stared at it, but it was no good; the name was not enough.

The woman watched him. Then she stood up, came around the table, pulled a chair close to him, and sat down. She pushed the fork in under the food, lifted some into the air, and held it there.

"Things come full circle, don't they?" she said. She wasn't talking to him, but to a man sitting across the table. He didn't know the man. "How many times do you think Dad fed me? And now..."

He took the food in his mouth. It tasted like nothing.

* * *

The sun was up above the trees as they left the apartment. They were hot and sweaty. Their bare feet slapped against the chipped gray paint of the wooden steps as they descended.

Madge wore one of the daring new bathing suits that revealed her shoulders and thighs. He wore only an old pair of work pants cut off at the knees. The sweat rolled down his chest, and he felt heavy with a pleasant, dreamy fatigue. Why was he so hot? It was not yet midday and not really that warm outside, even though the sun shone down brilliantly upon them as they walked south down the street.

In only a minute or two, they were on the beach. They ran hand in hand into the water. There was no seaweed, no stinging jellyfish. Madge dove through one wave, then another, then walked out of the water and lay down on the sand. He swam in the trough the waves parallel to the beach, back and forth, back and forth. But he couldn't stay apart from her for long.

Madge lay on her stomach with her head resting on her crossed arms. He lay down, forming a "T" with her, his head on the small of her back. Almost instantly his fatigue returned, and he fell asleep.

When he woke, he was warm again. He pressed his lips into the sweat glistening at the back of her knee. She woke up and they walked back into the water, but they didn't swim this time or take a wave. They let the water wash over them, wave after gentle wave.

When they came out, they were deliciously cool and hungry.

* * *

He turned left out of the bedroom and made his way down the hall, touching the wall with his fingertips as he went, as if to assure himself that the way was straight and he had not launched himself upon some unmapped expanse from which he could never return.

At the end of the hall, the floor broke up and fell away in a series of fragments that descended deeper, deeper into the distance.

What was this? Was there something he was supposed to do here? He couldn't remember. He edged his right foot forward until the ball of it was extended precariously over the edge of the precipice. Then he stopped, dizzy with fear and the fatigue of trying to remember. He wanted to go back, but go back where? He couldn't remember what was behind him. Maybe something worse than this falling away. He was afraid to turn around.

He stood there until he'd forgotten that he'd ever been anywhere else.

Finally, he heard a sound from somewhere beneath him. It rose toward him. Then he saw a woman down there. She was climbing the broken floor, but she stopped abruptly when she saw him.

She was a big-boned woman, tall with graying hair. She stood looking up at him for a moment; then she sagged against the wall.

She called out something and a man appeared. The man looked up at the woman, then up at him. The man climbed up beside the woman, put his arm around her, and hugged her. Then together, they came on up and, one on each side, helped him down the stairs.

Their touch was warm and comforting, and for a moment he wasn't frightened.

Her breasts in the cool, pearly light of morning looked like fresh cheese. He cupped them, one in each hand. Yes, they felt like round, soft cheeses. He lowered his head between them, rolled his face slowly back and forth across them. They didn't smell like cheese, though. They smelled like fried bacon! Madge smelled like fried bacon everywhere. He licked the smell of bacon off her breasts, licked it off everywhere he found it as she giggled at first, twitching beneath him, then lay still, then pulled him almost roughly over on top of her.

They made love the first time quickly and hungrily, as he had eaten his breakfast of bacon and eggs only a few moments before. Afterwards, they lay on their sides facing each other, chests heaving, eyes bright, as if they'd just finished one race, but were not tired at all, and were ready to run another.

When they made love the second time, it was slower than the first, less frenzied, but warmer, wetter, deeper, more powerful, a rolling slow-motion explosion. Afterward they slept.

When they woke, the sun was higher and brighter outside, and the room was filled with warmth and the smell of the ocean, which they could hear surging softly in the near distance.

The third time they made love slowly, slowly. They would stop to talk, not about the past or their plans for the future, but just about this moment, as if it was all there was, forever. Then they began again, slowly, then faster, then slow, fast, slow, concentrating on the flesh they held and the flesh they were.

When they finished, they were exhausted and the sheet was dark with sweat. They pulled it off the bed and, each holding two corners, they whipped it back and forth in the warm and humid room. In the end the sheet was still wet and they were panting in the heat.

"Let's go for a swim," he said.

* * *

He was in a different place now. A man and a woman had brought him here. They walked on either side of him, supporting him. In this place were many other very old people. Some looked up at him as he walked between the man and the woman. Some did not.

The man and the woman seemed worried and sad, but he wasn't. Already he had begun to forget that this was a different place.

* * *

He woke up before Madge and guessed from the cool, diffuse, pearly light that it must still be early.

It's going to be a good Saturday. He received his paycheck the day before, and after dinner he and Madge are going to meet their best friends, John and Tessy Brennan, at the Playland. It will be great fun, but it is the morning that he is looking forward to.

The first thing they bought with his pay last night was bacon and eggs. They are in the icebox. He makes a movement on the bed, and Madge opens her eyes.

"I'm hungry," he says. She smiles and yawns as she slowly wipes the sleep from her eyes.

After breakfast they make love *three times*. They are so young, so much in love.

The apartment grows warmer and warmer from the rising sun and their lovemaking. Madge puts on her bathing suit and he his old cut-off work pants, and they walk the short block down to Rockaway beach. They play in the cool, clean water and then sleep on the sand. When they wake up, they're hot again, so they walk back into the water and stand touching fingertips, the water washing over them until they are almost cold.

After the beach, they go back to their apartment to change, then walk north up Tyrone Street toward Doyle's Steak House. The sun is high and bright and hot in the sky, but their hair is still wet from the ocean, and they are deliciously cool.

Standing across the street, they have to cup their hands around their eyes and squint against the sun glaring off the front window of Doyle's, but then they see it. The slatted blinds are raised. They will not have to wait.

GOTTA GO BABY DOLL
Sande Smith

"Stand still sweetie," I said while I held on to her wrist. Her fingers tap tapped in a steady rhythm as if tiny cymbals were attached to them and she was keeping time to a tune that only she could hear. She was hard to grasp now; bone and sinew had eclipsed her plumpness. I felt as if she would slip from my fingers. Yes, it was difficult for me to accept this new thinness, to let go of the way she used to be – round-bellied with full soft arms.

I have captured her for this moment, interrupted her never-ending walk through the house. It is this perpetual walking up and down the stairs, through the house, that has succeeded in melting away the creamy coffee-colored flesh from her bones – something she longed to achieve through constant dieting when I was a teenager.

I have come to know her journey well. How she goes through the living room and picks up magazines, opens the drawers in the dining room to remove silverware and table cloths, carries them with her as she walks up the sixteen stairs painted brown, now peeling so that the green peeks through, clutches the forks in her hands that often ache with the arthritic remnants of rheumatic fever. She enters the bathroom and lays two forks down on the pale blue sink. That is where I will find them, laid out as if they were the finishing touches on a table setting.

She will put the seat down on the toilet, then head out to stop by my bedroom door, which I keep closed tight to prevent her explorations. She will place her palm against the door as if to listen with them to make sure that I am well, then she will back away to stride down the hall – the green skin of its linoleum gouged by heel marks.

As she moves toward her own room, which faces onto the busy street, loud with the sounds of girls laughing while they double Dutch skip and men clinking their bottles wrapped in paper bags, she will pass my sister's room, now empty because we fought so much over how to take care of our mother.

* * *

I have captured her because it is time for her to go to day care and time for me to go to my job as an editor of a women's publication at a non-profit organization. I helped her to put her thin arms into the blue denim jacket that clutches her narrow waist. She grabbed the stretchy knit hat from my hands and pulled it down over her Afro, which grows wild and frothy soft.

"I'll have to call Dad and have him cut your hair," I murmured as I buttoned her coat. Dad hardly came to the house anymore, probably because he was not comfortable with seeing his ex-wife, formerly an analytical woman who could peer into the soul of anyone she met, change into a docile sweet creature that just wanted to walk through the house, eat tasty foods, and be hugged. My Dad also didn't like going to funerals. He preferred not to see people on their final leave taking. Although I didn't connect the two things then – the change in my mother and funerals – I connect them now.

When the bus for day care pulled up outside our house and honked, I said, "Come on."

"Ok, baby doll," she answered. "Here I come." She clicked her tongue, making a kind of happy sound, then walked out onto the porch, lifting her thin legs energetically – as if she were warming up for her part in the chorus line. Then, she waved her hand at a young kid walking by. We have lived here so long (30 years) that she knows everyone, at least by sight. Yet while I was growing up, she was never very social, preferring to keep to herself in the house with my sister and me enshrined in our books as we studied for a better future.

But once she got Alzheimer's all that changed. It was as if she began to consider herself an ambassador. Everyone who passed by belonged in her kingdom, this narrow street crammed with row homes.

When my mother lost the ability to speak in logical, linear syntax, I was afraid – afraid of losing hold of that which defined our relationship. My mother had always been unerringly certain of the rightness of her actions. She

41

would never let on that she felt confused. She told me what to do and how. But then all that changed. From the moment I decided to go 600 miles away from home to college, I began to realize that there were journeys I would have to take without my mother. And when I returned home from college, I saw that there were journeys that my mother would take without me.

* * *

"Come on," I said. "Time to get on the bus." She started down the concrete steps obediently enough, but then when she noticed the bus, she seized hold of the black metal railing with both hands. "No," she said, shaking her head resolutely.

This amazed me. How could she still have such resistance, such strength of will to refuse me? I looked down the street, pierced with thin trees, cracked sidewalk, porches where people sat and watched one another when they walked by, or chatted together from across their wooden banisters. Then I looked back at my mother. This is the house that she yearned for. An orphan from the time she was 12, she had lived in an uncle's house, then a husband's house, then a second husband's house, and finally the house of the mother of her third husband.

My father, her third husband, found this house for her, constructed 50 years ago, in a neighborhood that used to be Polish. This row home the color of burnt red brick pressed between its neighbors had been her promised land. Soon after she moved in though, she began to talk about how ugly it was. "I'll never be able to make this house into something nice," she'd say.

One day, I asked my Dad why he had imprisoned her there. He shook his head and said, "I didn't know that she didn't like it. The people who lived there before were sorry they sold it to us. They wanted to buy it back."

* * *

"Come on Mom, time to go to day care." I heard my voice rising.

"No," she repeated. Her jaw tightened in that way that I recognized from my childhood when I had talked back and she was about to give me a backhand lick, or worse. In those days, her eye would narrow too and she'd become fierce; her voice would harden, and I could almost hear a growl underneath her words. If I didn't obey, and quickly, then I would be sent to fetch the clothesline coiled in the linen bag on the washing machine. Oh yeah, I knew that look.

"Come on Mom, they're waiting for you," I said, and I felt my left eye narrow into an angry slit like hers. "I have to get ready for work," I thought. "I still haven't eaten breakfast. I can't miss my train because I have to finish that story for the next issue and meet with the graphic designer."

Out loud I cajoled, "Come on sweetie, you have to go. I have to get to my job."

This is not the first time she has made my blood boil with her stubbornness. One week she decided that she was a police officer. This idea was touched off by a letter that came in the mail addressed to her, because for twenty years she had worked as an employee of the Philadelphia government – 10 years as an orderly in the State Hospital for the Mentally insane and 10 years as a nurse at the Philadelphia General Hospital. She used to tell me how much she loved her job holding premature babies, nursing them to health.

On this particular day, she pushed open the screen door, ran down the steps, and strode up and down the street in her slippers. When I said, "Let's go in the house," she said, "Don't you touch me; I'm a police officer." I finally had to flag down a police car and ask the officers to bring her into the house. She took the arm of the younger one, a tall brown-skinned fellow, smiled demurely, and explained that she too was an officer. As I watched them step onto the porch together, I had to shake my head with admiration at how charming she was, and my anger slowly dissolved.

* * *

"No," she said again, gripping the railing tighter. She was not about to be fooled by my put-on kindness. The other day care goers – gray haired and docile – pressed their faces against the bus window. My raven-haired, step-lively, dazzling mother shook her head like a rebellious stallion and held fast to the railing. My face began to heat up with embarrassment and rancor. I tried to pry her fingers, one by one, off the railing.

Her fingers, gnarled from arthritis, were tipped with brittle nails growing out over soft pads. Even the pads were drying out, wrinkling a bit at the ends like your fingers do when you soak in the tub too long.

Every time I un-pried one or two fingers, she grabbed hold again. I began to feel guilty, and she held on even tighter. "I don't understand," I hissed. "What's wrong with day care? Why won't you go?"

"No, don't want to. Don't want to."

Despite a history of pain in her joints, she had never been vain about her hands, preferring to suffer their troubles valiantly, martyr-like. When I was little, she would clean the sink without gloves. "Do you think you're better than I am?" she would say when I showed signs of squeamishness about the garbage wet in the sink. "These hands have done it all," she'd brag. Hands that diapered four children. Hands that soothed premature babies. Hands that held three husbands and threw them away when they abused, when they neglected, when they disappointed. Hands that accepted the twists and turns of fate, and said *whatever*. Hands that said *come here sugar plum*. Hands that taught me that touch spoke truer than words. Hands that told you when you were in the presence of love.

These hands, draining of fullness like the rest of her, spoke their own language that became more emphatic than the words her mind could force through her lips. Every morning when I remembered, I would start the day by rubbing her hands with lotion, but the results were temporary, short-lived. She was drying out from the inside, becoming like a leaf still lingering on the tree, beautiful, yet brittle, veins jutting out from the paper dry flesh.

Now feeling very much like a villain, aware of the eyes on the porches pressing into my skin, the other day care attendees watching from the bus, my stomach about to heave with anxiety, I let go and looked at her. Her chin was set tight. Her eyes scoured me with their intensity. I felt as if I could hear her speaking to me: *They trap me there. I cannot roam around as I like. I do not know these people. I'm fine here. This is my home. I know this place. Look there is*

Sheri going down the street, and there is Stacy, and look at that girl pushing her baby in the stroller. I know these people and people who look just like them.

I spoke sternly, "You know I don't like to leave you here alone. I worry about you."

"No," she said again, gripping the railing tighter. I felt like she was filling my head with her plea: *I know every inch of this house, the walls, the creaking floor boards, the linoleum that is scuffed from your heels when you ran through the upstairs hall. I know this place as well as my body, except my body is changing while this house remains the same.*

* * *

"Alright" I said. "Ok, you win. But just for today, tomorrow you're going. I don't care if I have to carry you onto that bus." I would show her. She wasn't the only one who could have an attitude.

I waved the bus driver on, then stomped up the stairs and opened the screen door to the house. She looked around her as if to make sure the bus was indeed leaving, and then she said, "Wait, baby doll, wait," and followed me into the house. My oatmeal was burning. The sound of my banging the pots on the stove lured her into the kitchen.

Even though she had already eaten, seeing the food excited her appetite. And so I spooned some of the oatmeal into a bowl and placed it on the table. But I wasn't ready to answer her happy go lucky smile with one of my own. I was still mad.

I talked to her while we ate, my voice harsh. "Now I have to lock you in all day. You know I don't feel good about locking you in."

My caseworker, the person who had told me about the senior day care center, had reinforced my fear that a fire might break out and then she'd be trapped. If day care wasn't going to work, then I knew I'd have to consider a nursing home. I had sworn that I would never do that; I would never abandon her to strangers. But I was afraid that I would come home one day and the house would have burned to the ground with her in it – afraid she would

45

know I was a bad daughter and not love me anymore – afraid she wouldn't know me anymore.

While I was still eating my oatmeal, she got up, circled the round table where I sat, then stopped behind me. She patted my shoulder gently, and when I reached up to grasp her hand, she squeezed tight and said, "Don't worry sugar plum." Then tap tapping her fingers, she said, "Gotta go baby doll," and set off to journey through the house that she knew so well, leaving me to take my own journey, the touch of her hand imprinted on my skin.

THE LIST
Kate LeSar

He checked his front pants pocket. Good. It was there, his list. And he'd remembered to look for it. Maybe he'd stopped slipping. Maybe...maybe he wouldn't get any worse.

He pulled the list out. Only one item was written on it: "jewelry store." Yes! He'd known when he woke up that he wanted to do something important today. And this was it. The jewelry store.

He slipped into his boat shoes and looked at the bed. Kathleen was already up. He used to get up before her, but now she was always out of bed first. He wanted to find her, to make sure she was home.

He left the bedroom. "Kathleen, Kathleen, where are you?"

She stood at the counter in the kitchen with...the big round blue thing...and a spoon. She turned around and smiled at him. She was so beautiful. He walked toward her.

"Good morning. How did you sleep?"

He stopped. How did he sleep? What did she mean? "In the bed. You were there too, Kathleen. Then you got up. I slept in the bed."

She turned back to the big round thing, the bowl. He remembered now. The bowl. He put his arms around her waist. "You smell good. I love you so much."

"Oh Robert. Robert. I love you too. I'm making pancakes. Blueberry. Your favorite."

His favorite? Yes, she was right. He'd always loved blueberry pancakes.

"Here. Put these two place mats and utensils on the table on the lanai."

"Lanai?"

"The screened-in porch, Robert. Right out there. See the wide door. Walk through there."

He took the rolled bundle she gave him and went outside. The Marco River was calm this morning, but the sky was gray. It could rain. He should check the boat. Make sure it was tied securely. He headed to the screen door leading out to the dock and took hold of the handle, but the door wouldn't open. He put the bundle down on the concrete and used both hands. The door still wouldn't open. Rusted probably. He went back into the house to go into the garage.

"Where are you going, Robert?"

"To the garage."

"We're going to have breakfast in just a few minutes. Why don't you wait."

"No, I need..." What was it he needed? He couldn't remember now. He looked at her, but her back was to him. He went to her and hugged her tight. She felt warm against his chest.

"Careful, Robert, I'm cooking the pancakes."

* * *

Kathleen put the plate in front of him. He picked up the spoon and cut a bite of pancake.

"Wait, sweetheart. I heated the maple syrup the way you like it. Shall I pour it for you?"

He shook his head. "I can pour it myself." He poured the syrup and ate the pancakes and drank the coffee.

He was supposed to do something. He tried to think. He tried really hard. He couldn't remember. He was losing his mind, his good mind. He wasn't a surgeon anymore. He couldn't operate. He had something to do today though, something special.

"More pancakes, Robert?"

He looked at his plate. It was clean. He shook his head. "No, I have to do something."

Kathleen kept eating.

"Do you know what I have to do?"

"No. Today isn't your golf day. That's tomorrow. With Fred and Howard."

Fred and Howard. Two other doctors. Old friends. Golf. Good. He still played golf. He stood and wandered over to look at the water. "That's it! The boat, Kathleen. I have to check the boat." He tried the screen door. It still stuck.

"And fix the door. It needs to be oiled." He started toward the house, but Kathleen stood and put her arms around him.

"Andrew took the boat up to Fort Myers for servicing. It will take a few weeks to get everything done."

Andy took the boat? His son Andy? "Did I ask him to? I don't remember."

"That's okay."

"Is it...broken?"

"No, the boat just needs to be serviced. You know how they have to take the motor apart and clean it. Power-wash the bottom. Make little repairs, like the cracked lid on the life jacket bin. I dropped the anchor on it, remember? All that maintenance takes a while to finish."

Someone had dropped the anchor. Robert had a vague picture of an accident, but the details wouldn't come. He looked at Kathleen. She didn't add anything, just gave him an odd smile. The picture faded. "You must be right, Kitty. 'We've always had the Jenny Lynn serviced every year or two."

"Oh, Robert, you remembered the boat's name. You named it for Jennifer when she was just a baby. Jenny Lynn, Andy's first little girl."

She hugged him tight. It felt so good. He hugged her back. That felt even better. He put his hand on her breast. "Let's go to bed, Kathleen."

* * *

He woke up. Kathleen was still in bed. He remembered. Oh Lord, he remembered. Sweet Kathleen. His sweet Kathleen. He got up quietly, picked up his trousers from the floor, and left the room.

In the kitchen he put on his trousers, then reached into his pocket and pulled out the paper. Jewelry store. He had to go now. But where were his car keys? In the bedroom? What about Kathleen's? He looked around. Her purse was there, on the table. He found her keys. He held the paper and the car keys in one hand and went to the door that led to the garage. The door wouldn't open. He turned the knob again. And again. Mustn't wake Kathleen. But it wouldn't budge. He couldn't even open the door. He sat down on the chair by the door and put his face in his hands.

49

"Robert? I didn't hear you get up. What's wrong?"

He looked up. Kathleen stood in front of him, wearing her blue robe. "I can't open the door."

"Oh, Robert. Do you need something from the garage?"

He nodded.

"What do you need?"

He shook his head. He hated this. "I don't know."

She knelt in front of him. "Let's check your list. It's in your hand. And my car keys. How did you...oh, I left my bag on the table. Anyway, here, I'll hold the keys. Do you want to show me your list?"

He handed the list and the keys to her.

"Jewelry store. Do you want to go to the jewelry store?"

"Yes. I have to go now."

"Why? Do you need to buy something?"

He looked at her and tried to think. Of course he had to buy something. "I can't tell you. It's a secret."

She smiled at him and rubbed her cheek against his. "After that nice lovemaking, I hope you don't have another girlfriend?"

He smiled back at her. Kathleen always made him smile. "You're my only girlfriend, Kitty. I have to go though, before I...before I forget."

"Okay. Let me get dressed and I'll drive you." Kathleen stood up. "Oh, the breakfast dishes. They can wait, I guess."

"I can drive myself. Give me the keys."

"I need to run some errands too, Robert. I'll drop you at the jeweler's and then pick you up. The schedule will work out just fine."

"No. I don't want you to drive me. I will drive myself. I will drive my car. Give me back the keys."

He stood and held out his hand.

She had a funny look. She didn't look like his Kathleen. "I can't do that, Robert. Doctor Wolfe said you shouldn't drive."

Dr. Wolfe? Who was Dr. Wolfe? "Why did he say that? I can see."

"Oh, Robert, I know. Your vision is fine. But...sweetheart, it's your illness. The one that makes you forget a few things. That's why you can't drive. But you're doing very well. You have a medication that helps you. Look. Here's your list. You remembered to write down the

50

jewelry store. That shows how well you're doing. Now let me get dressed."

"I want to drive." He felt like crying. But men don't cry. Men drive cars. Kathleen put her arms around him. He began to cry and he heard her crying too.

THE DANCE
Katie Cameron

I'll hold you like a scarf
close to me, dancing.
I'll drape a part of you
around my waist,
put a corner of you
across my shoulder, weary,
then swing slowly
around this quiet room.

Let's try holding you to the
light, scan
your faint imprint
like a shroud.
Your deep colors fade
to a pastel you never were,
and behind
shadows move, but sadly
no features, no laugh –
I am forgetting.

I barely remember,
and you cannot remember.
That must be it.
Here! Mother!
A banner for the day
we learned to love each other.
You are pressed to my chest,
hammered by exactly
two tears.

AFTER LEAVING
Torie Olson

Mick has been locked out of his bedroom for calling his new lover, Rebecca, by his old lover's name, Annie. Mick knows Becca is in there having murderous thoughts, even though, as an attorney, she is opposed to capital punishment. He also knows crying out for Annie is no proof of a crime – he is not double dipping as Becca imagines. Naming Annie as he loses himself in Becca's body is just a remembrance. Such is the hypnotic power of love.

The over-designed, Italian couch is not a comfortable one, so Mick is already up and dressed. He has had to paw through the laundry pile for clothes because his closet is off-limits, too. This is not a good day to recycle yesterday's shirt. It is already too hot for hot coffee, and it is only 6:00 a.m.

Mick is alarmed when the phone rings because it is too early for ordinary news. But he is relieved to hear the voice of his mother's neighbor; she is calling from Minnesota where it is two hours later. Thank God, it is not his son Cody in trouble. Or Annie. He will never stop feeling responsible for Annie either. Some things are just unconditional. Love, guilt, whatever....

Mick figures the neighbor is planning a trip to San Francisco and wants a tour guide, but as he drops an ice cube into the raku tea bowl he is using as a coffee cup, he hears her say, "I have to talk to you about your mother." Then she lowers her voice as if she is worried the wrong person might hear. "Claire walked the dog without her skirt on yesterday. She went around the block in her underwear."

Mick's shiver is audible two thousand miles away. There has been a shift in parameters.

* * *

53

Once Mick and his older brother, Jonah, had been the ones wearing nothing but the chill air. They built a huge nest in a pile of leaves, and Claire had come, shaking overalls at them like bright, red flags. "Haven't you forgotten something," she'd demanded angrily.

"Birds are naked," Jonah had insisted, lying on his back and heaping on more leaves until only his head was above the hill of scarlet that used to dress the trees.

"Birds have feathers," Mick had explained, the mediator, even at three.

But Jonah had continued to bait their mother, "And what about fish?"

"Fish are numb!" she'd shouted, before diving into the leafy shelter after her sassiest son.

* * *

"It's very fall-like here...cold and rainy," the neighbor continues, as if hot weather could be a mitigating factor. "Something's got to be done. You better come home, dear. And bring your raingear." Before hanging up she warns, "Don't be surprised – Claire's become, well, difficult."

From Mick's point of view, Claire has always been difficult. That is a constant; it is something he expects. Despite his mother's creative threats and attempts at bribery, he visits only one week in fifty-two, and for years, he'd dragged Annie and their son, Cody, along as buffers. He will not bother to ask Rebecca. She wouldn't come in any case; she has no interest in the past.

Sometimes Mick feels as if his brother (who drowned in the ice-covered lake at age ten) is the one that got away. His father's the one who was thrown away, as were two other successive, short-lived husbands. Mick's the only one left who can be called home to mother his mother. There is no one else.

When he checks in that night, Claire sounds normal, but this is not evidence enough to discount her neighbor's testimony. Over the last two years, Claire has been losing her senses one by one. The first to go was her hearing, so she began talking more and listening less. Then she couldn't smell how much perfume she had on or how old the garbage was. Lately she says the food tastes bland, so she's down to 104 pounds. She sends holiday checks and postcards in triplicate; she calls *ad nauseum* about her will – about what she should give to so and so, and what she should leave to Mick. And should she do it now? Or should she wait and do it posthumously? She likes to say that word, posthumously; it always makes Mick think of the word "humus," like the decaying pile she has always hoarded like gold for her garden.

Claire often calls when he and Becca are in bed. Mick thinks his mother has some kind of psychic timing. Becca has no trouble screening calls, but Mick just doesn't have it in him to let the phone ring. Of course, talking to his mother always terminates his interest in sex, which once made Rebecca snipe angrily, "She already has a dog, doesn't she?"

"Yeah, so?"

"So what's the point of acting like one? She holds out a scrap and you're there."

He'd pulled his oxford blue shorts back on and turned on the light to read a mountaineering story with a bad outcome – his favorite genre. He was trying to make it clear that he was not going to have this conversation, but Rebecca wasn't done yet. She scrounged around the sheets for her underpants, yanked a silk camisole over her head, and then instructed, "You need to learn the difference between a fake throw and a real one."

"Yeah, well, she is my mother," thinks Mick. He flies east.

Annie is the one who drives him to the airport because his keys are locked in the bedroom with Becca. In this heat, Annie manages to look great in the white Victorian slip she is wearing as a dress. Mick eyes her and thinks, "definitely prettier than Rebecca."

At the curb in front of Northwest Airlines, Annie reaches for Mick's hand, peels his fingers open, and places a vial of ginkgo pills in his palm.

"For memory loss," she explains, "...the latest rage in Europe...no awful side effects."

Up in the air, Mick considers the fact that his mother has not asked for help and is unlikely to accept it. He plays with the remedy he has put in his pocket, but he does not believe in miracles. As he hangs in the air over the heartlands and Great Lakes, he considers catching the next plane back.

The pilot touches down smoothly on a runway flooded with light. It's a harsh light, the kind that often trails big storms and leaves an impression of impending metamorphosis upon the landscape. Mick looks for his prescription Ray Bans in his briefcase.

The taxi drops him at his mother's house. The door is locked. He rings and rings, but there is no answer. He walks around to the back where the dog barks shrilly and lunges at the gate. He speaks some soothing words and is allowed entrance, but the Yorky stays at his heels, yipping with suspicion.

Through the big picture window he sees Claire, fully dressed with a string of heirloom pearls around her neck. She appears somehow diminished, smaller and grayer than Mick remembers, and her clothing seems to float on her body. Mick knocks on the window, and Claire leaves the clutter of papers on her desk, crosses the Tabriz carpet, which is as big as a swimming pool, and opens the back door.

"Where am I?" she whispers into her son's ear as he gives her a hug. Mick holds onto her in order to sustain the moment before he has to answer her question. Claire breaks away and pats her clothing back into place. A dark cloud moves in and there's a crackle of thunder. "It's like a different world here," she says, gesturing at her jungle-like back garden. "In 71 years, I've never seen a Minnesota summer so green or so wet."

The sky lets loose and Mick drags his bag inside. Rain comes streaming from the eaves. "Don't bother to unpack," Claire commands. "We're going to the lake."

* * *

For a change, Claire doesn't insist on driving. She makes it clear in subtle, possessive statements that this is no transfer of power; she has just misplaced her glasses. Mick is sure his mother has no trouble seeing things in the distance and that her glasses are only for reading, but he lets it go. He puts on his own wire rims and the world beyond the windshield comes into a watery focus.

Mick knows the road backwards and forwards; he could drive it in his sleep, having made this trip north every summer of his childhood. It was the annual migration back to his mother's ancestral territory. Their father never made the trip, but rather, he seemed to welcome the break in a mercurial marriage. Mick and his brother Jonah fought over things like who got to fill the gas tank, wash the windshield, and who got to ride shotgun. What they really wanted was to be in the driver's seat. They were in such a hurry to grow up, to be the ones in control, to give or withhold.

Mick maneuvers his mother's Saab through the storm and wracks his brain for a safe topic of conversation. Weather has always been neutral ground, so he asks for details about the summer flooding.

"It's been raining frogs and fishes. All anybody talks about. Hear it on the radio, hear it at parties, hear it in church. According to the minister, the flood is to remind us of something we've forgotten."

"What's that?"

"I forget."

When Mick turns sharply, Claire laughs at him, and the skin around her eyes creases like wrinkled linen. "Oh, you know, the Noah analogy," she continues. "If we're not pious, we better be really good swimmers."

"Are you still a member of the Loon Club?" Mick asks.

Claire gives a perfunctory nod. Her paternal grandfather named her the first "Loon-hearted One" – the Ojibway term for brave. To earn this title, you had to swim across the lake – a feat that required kinship with fish and water birds, as temperatures rarely rose out of the sixties. It's something you had to do at least once a year, if being loon-hearted was a personal goal.

Mick, Jonah, and their cousins were required to spend a certain portion of every summer in training. With Claire paddling behind in the canoe, their lips turned blue, their flesh crawled with goose bumps, and their imaginations seethed with four-foot eels, snapping turtles, and the big-toothed muskellunge – that whale of fresh water. They were little boys expected to conquer a lake, which of course, they eventually did, but Mick never felt brave, only coerced.

He follows the straight gray tarmac past desolate Finnish farms, their small houses drowning in huge square yards. In between the compulsively combed rows of corn, alfalfa, and soybeans, lay windbreaks of Norway pine or spruce and an occasional thicket of dead-looking tamarack. The lackluster landscape flattens his spirits. There is monotony and then more of it. This is suicide country.

Claire tells Mick that his grandfather used to drive his Pierce Arrow up here when the road was just a long flat ribbon of dirt. "It took all day, but the car was so high off the ground, I could see inside all the houses." She has her father's red tackle box on her lap. She opens it like a present and picks through it, taking inventory of all the heirloom leaders, poppers, and tufted jigs. She polishes the spoons on her sleeve, and fingers the feathery flies that mimic winged insects. She points out the ephemeridae in nymph, dun, and spinner stages that have teased the trophy and pan fish to the surface. She takes them in her palm, caressing the gossamer threads, their wings and thoraxes of marabou, elk hair, and rabbit, as if this gesture will gently wake each beautiful impostor.

Claire has taken every opportunity to dangle this box full of lures and tokens of promise in front of her sons, her nephews and her grandson. She's told them the family fish stories and made them covet its contents: "My grandfather caught the four-foot tiger with this big spoon. This long-winged streamer fly was my father's luckiest. In 1938, the caddis fly caught twenty-one fish before breakfast. My uncle liked the mayfly." She made them believe this was the tackle that would satisfy their wildest fish lust, and a few other genetic desires as well.

Mick notices that it has stopped raining and shuts off the wipers. The car seems tiny and close, even though it's just the two of them and the dog sleeping in the back. It is crowded with the ghosts of absent people.

Claire locks the box, and when she has settled it in the wheel well under her feet, she tells Mick that she's no longer speaking to her neighbor. "She says I'm getting dotty." When Mick fails to comment, Claire asks, "Well...what do *you* think?"

"You seem okay," Mick answers cagily, "but you do repeat yourself."

"Can't you live with that?"

"Sure. Can you?"

"Makes no difference to me!" Claire says, sitting up straight. "If you're losing your memory, you forget you don't remember," she adds, enunciating slowly, like she's talking to someone of little intelligence. Mick bites his tongue. Claire fingers her trademark pearls. It isn't her usual lake-wear; she's just forgotten to leave them in the city. His father used to say each pearl represented an irritation. They are large and they are many.

Other subjects are broached, some amiable, others argumentative. Mick fades in and out, as his mother launches a diatribe against Minnesota politicians, gives critical reviews of recent art exhibits and books, and goes on and on about the refrigerator repair man who will not get away with his blatantly inflated bill. She seems ready to kill over this.

Mick thinks of his last shouting match with an equally quick-tempered Rebecca, with Rebecca doing all the shouting, of course. "You have no right to sleepwalk through my life," she'd screamed. How soon her passion for him had turned to rage.

He and Claire drive through the Dairy Queen for Buster Bars, and Claire gnaws through her ice cream as if she hasn't eaten in a week. She's unresponsive as Mick shares his own news. "I'm doing some interesting pro bono work," he tells her. "Cody's made the row team at Harvard...Becca will probably leave me."

"Who's Becca and where are you going?" Claire interrupts, as if Mick has made a wrong turn. He is nonplused by his mother's sudden disorientation, but he keeps up a pretense of normalcy. "To the lake," he answers, as if this is news, too.

After several more miles of flat prairie, Mick is privy to a few more facts about Claire: "You know my mother died when she was 72, my father at 69. So at my age, the importance of memory becomes moot."

"Why's that?"

"Haven't you heard of the Law of Averages?"

"What's your point, Mother?"

"It's certainly obvious that at 71, I haven't got much longer on earth."

Mick is annoyed by his mother's patronizing tone. "That's ridiculous," he says. "You're in perfect health."

"Well!" Claire shoots back. "Who says you have to be sick to die?"

* * *

Before heading out to Blackberry Lake, they stop in the nearest town. The sun is setting in raspberry streamers over the green boxcars by the paper factory. Mick senses this display is only a pause between the deluges of rain. At his mother's bidding, he pulls into the Piggly Wiggly parking lot. He puts his driving glasses back in their case, and his eyes take a moment to readjust. He follows Claire through the electronic doors and pushes the silver cart up and down six aisles of chips and pop, looking for dinner. Driving the cart doesn't make him feel empowered. He is only pushing along the things his mother no longer wants to carry.

Mick has forgotten what you can buy in a north woods grocery. At the deli counter he inventories glorified rice, pea cheese, and five loaves of mystery meat, not to mention nine kinds of Jell-O salad. Rebecca would call him a fucking snob, and the synthetic ingredients would horrify Annie. His mother buys a case of beer, some crackers, and a smoked fish, then asks, "Where's Annie?"

"We broke up," he tells her, deciding not to add the words, "two years ago" to his response. That would only be asking for a defensive reaction.

Still she says snottily, "If you're going to leave someone, you don't wait twenty years to do it." Another one of Claire's hard and fast rules, but Mick realizes that, again, her math is correct. He and Annie were together for almost half their lives.

Next stop is the bait shop at Jackpine Junction, just a mile from the house. This establishment is full of men in camouflage jackets and caps. Mick nods at them, but they do not return his greeting. The walls are festooned with deer, wildcat, and muskies glaring out of glass eyes. "Frankly, I'd rather be cremated," Claire confides, "Although there are people who'd probably like to put my head right up there alongside that bull-moose."

Claire is not well liked in this county. She's too territorial, and the locals do not forgive her posted land, her pressed charges against trespassers, or her campaigns

60

against development. The hunters narrow their eyes at her as if they've spotted a new target. Claire glares back. Her Wellingtons squeak on the speckled linoleum floor as she turns on her heel and says grandly, "I'll be in the car."

Mick takes his time, surveying the bins of floating frogs, chubs, crappies, and fatheads wriggling under the big, block-lettered sign that reads, *Guaranteed to catch fish or die trying.* His gaze travels up the wall of neon cicadas, red-eye wigglers, slowpoke jigs, and fuzz-e-grubbs. They are not the treasures of his grandfather's box; they lack the patina that comes with age and memory. Mick thinks, "Any fish with half a brain could see right through those brassy promises." He buys some Dr. Juice (his family's preferred fish-catching potion) and some live leeches.

He walks up and down the row of parked American sedans and pick-up trucks. He does this twice to make sure. He rummages in his pocket for his glasses and looks again. Claire has driven off. Claire has left him at the junction, and Mick is just as startled as he was all those years ago, when his ten year-old brother had pulled a similar act.

* * *

A few days before the accident, before the runaway car ran Jonah into the pond, Mick had the sense that his family was living in a house of leaves, a house that could fly apart at any moment. As his parents argued on and on, Mick hid in his room with his hands over his ears. But he heard the Thunderbird roar away.

When Jonah had heard more than he could take, he'd swiped Claire's alligator bag and her keys. He'd driven off to Milkmaid's where he was finally found trying to forget his troubles at the sundae bar.

* * *

Mick is glad to be wearing rubber boots as he walks the sodden mile with the smelly bait to Cedar Point. Lichens climb the white birches like green ladders. The forest floor is rife with red caps and chanterelles that have erupted through pine needles and leaf mold. Fireweed, pink vetch, and wild morning glories smell sweeter in the damp. Rocks have grown moss like pregnant women grow hair, and the naked stones sweat. A lakeside path that was underfoot is now under water. Nothing's gone; it's just hidden.

The lots here are 25-acre parcels of woodland with lake frontage. Claire owns four that stretch around a point. Norton, a year-rounder, hails Mick as he nears his fence line. He's wearing a canvas hat adorned with a lopsided button. When Mick gets close enough, he can see that it says, *I'm Looking For a Good Piece of Bass*, which makes him remember just why Annie always found this man so offensive.

"Hope you're cooking tonight," Norton says, by way of greeting. He talks about the last supper he had at Claire's: "Thought the stew smelled a little funny. I was sick as a dog that night. She called me the next day to tell me her ice wasn't freezing. God knows how long her fridge had been on the blink."

"Other than that," Mick asks warily, "has she been all right?"

Norton looks him over through coke bottle glasses. "You're thinking Alzheimer's aren't you?" Then he pronounces his own diagnosis: "Well, I'm thinking 'Sometimer's.' Mostly, she seems just fine."

As Mick walks to the end of the road, he wonders when exposing yourself, getting lost, and poisoning your neighbor stops being "just fine." He can see the water through the trees now. He can make out the big log cabin, the boathouse, and the two-story garage where he and Jonah and the cousins used to sleep upstairs on feather beds. From the gate he can see the Saab parked under the towering cedars and his mother floating in the canoe out on the lake.

Mick walks out the long dock into the watery landscape. The lake and the sky at dusk are so monochromatic that it's hard to tell where one begins and the other lets off. As the duckboards creak and sway under his footfalls, he looks out over the vast gray area where the elements are in flux. The picture is soft and blurred, the dreamscape of a somnambulist.

Every five summers Mick's family has added another ten-foot section of dock. The staggered dates are marked in red marine paint, beginning with 1920. Claire says that when you walk to the end of her dock, you are walking toward the future.

Mick can pin different events to different sections. He knows the milestones of five generations like a litany. It's like a timeline in that way – grandfather died here, brother drowned here, father gone for good. These sections are like stepping on sharp stones, but he knows he can always return to a place before death and disappearance. There are also the sections that mark the better years – passing the bar, Cody being born, the first decade of Annie – when she'd wanted him so much the buttons of her dresses flew open of their own accord. He thinks now of her sweet breasts, soft as pink feathers.

Claire spots Mick and waves her paddle before heading in with strong J-strokes. The water glitters like sequins in the scarce last light. A loon crash lands between mother and son, feet first like a pontoon plane, and then cuts its flat reflection with its beak and makes a dive.

Mick has always envied these ancient birds their long breath and winters in the tropics. He's been awed by their perfect mastery of two realms, watching them journey through air and water with equal grace. He and Jonah used to spend summer nights practicing their wails and yodels and tremolos. They'd used these calls like a thieves' language to find each other in the dark. Jonah had been fascinated by their methods of escape, especially a sinking technique where tightly folded wings compressed air inside their bodies, enabling them to disappear without a ripple.

As Mick waits for the loon to resurface, he imagines it plummeting through two hundred feet of water after jewel-backed fish. Claire points behind her and the loon emerges on cue. It shakes its slick black head and preens its necklace of white feathers. They have played this guessing game for years, and Claire always wins, never a son, never a cousin. It's uncanny how she has always known where the diver will rise.

"Right again," she calls through the inky dusk.

* * *

When Mick was eight, he'd waited for his brother to rise. There were three of them, pinned to the mud bottom by that big whale of a car. Sara Day had come up for air, and Sara's mother had surfaced, too, but Jonah, Jonah was nowhere to be seen. With every breath, Mrs. Day had begged him to get help. But Mick had been magnetized by crystals of ice; stuck to that frozen barrier between himself and his brother, between gray sky and gray pond, between stinging air and numbing water – transfixed by Hypnos, Brother to Death – and he could not move.

* * *

It starts to pour as Mick and Claire pull the heavy wooden canoe out and carry it to the boathouse. They hoist it onto its cradle and race up the swampy path to the cabin. The green limbs of birch trees flail at the air. The lake shivers behind them.

Mick places a triangle of dry logs in the fireplace, adding strips of paper and a teepee of kindling. The massive stone chimney is draped with Ojibway medallions beaded round with flowers, stars, and eagles. They have hung there as far back as Mick can remember, along with a white-dotted loon wing and the family photos on the mantel. Mick can remember when his father's photo was plucked off the shelf, shredded like some old news, and burnt in the hearth. His son's photo had never even made it to the mantel, despite the scores of pictures Annie had sent to Claire. Mick is only there by the seat of his pants: He and Jonah at five and seven, fishing with their grandfather. He turns this photo over and sees their names in his mother's script, but their birth dates are wrong. All the other photos have also been recently labeled, including the one of his great-grandfather and the Chippewa trading furs. Those dates are probably wrong as well; when memory vanishes, history goes with it.

Mick and his mother tend to the cabin now – turning on the hot water, setting the seventy-year-old black walnut table, making the beds with Hudson Bay blankets – but the rituals seem old and empty. Mick finds notes pinned to the linens: *Dirty!* or *Clean!*; above the stove: *Turn Off Burners!*; taped to a cabinet: *Rat Poison, Not Kibbles!*; in the wood box: *Open Damper!*; and stuck to the refrigerator: *Freeze Perishables!* He pours sour milk down the drain, throws out a lemon coated with green fuzz, puts his take-out carton of leeches on the top shelf, and wonders if this is all as freaky as it seems. He wishes Annie were here. For twenty years, she'd been his reality check.

Jonah always swore by the old leech in the bottle barometer: If the leech climbs into the neck, rain is imminent; if it lies coiled on the bottom, fine weather's coming. When Mick opens the paper carton the next morning, the leeches are climbing the walls and the lake is a mirror full of clouds.

Around noon Mick and Claire load the Alumacraft with their fishing gear, a six-pack of Leinenkugel's, a bar of orange cheese, and a box of stale Triscuits. Claire turns on the little electric trolling motor and heads for Seagull Flats. When it begins to drizzle, Mick says, "Maybe we'll need that ark after all."

"We wouldn't get in."

"Not good enough?"

"We're not a pair."

Claire drops anchor amidst green-tipped reeds that are bent like Indian bows. She takes sections of bamboo rod out of a leather case and slips them together. Then she opens the red metal box, ties on a fly, and sends it forward and back, slowly increasing the length of her cast over gray water dimpled by rain. She'd taught Mick and Jonah that fishing is something that takes one's full concentration. "It may look like you're doing nothing," she had lectured. "But when you send that line out, you have to put your whole being into it. It's the least you can do for a fish that is giving up its life for you."

Claire dangles her mayfly like a pendulum, and her eyes dart over the surface of the water, waiting for something to rise. Right away she pulls in a sunny with a yellow underbelly and a black spot by its gill. It's big enough to be an eater, but she throws it back anyway, and Mick follows the artful script of his mother's cast as the line is played again.

Claire whispers while she fishes. During the space of an hour, she tells the same stories two and three times. Mick pulls in two blue gills and later a small mouth, while early memories fall from his mother's lips, incessant as the rain.

Claire seems to have lost interest in fishing. Still, she catches a ten-inch northern. After she has threaded it on the stringer, her tone changes and she begins to speak of things Mick has not heard before: of stealing a garnet brooch, of all the sparrows she'd shot for nothing, of premarital dalliances in the boathouse and later deceits.

Despite the urgent, confessional tone, Mick feels powerless to absolve her. He'd like to forgive Claire her failings as a parent – her inflated expectations, her broken promises, her masked grief – but these things are not mentioned.

Claire pulls a fourteen-inch walleye from the lake and exhibits it smugly, as if it were the very thing she was after. A good fish compensates for a lot.

Mick is tired of listening and angry that he and Jonah are no longer topics of conversation. He wishes someone would tell their lives back to Claire and record them in memory again. It is devastating to be the only one who remembers. Mick interrupts the second telling of the stolen jewel and says, "I want to hear a story about Jonah."

Claire looks away, her eyes on the water with that same darting look. Although she's no longer fishing, she's still waiting for something to rise. She pops a beer and eats a cracker before finally saying, "You tell me one."

* * *

This is the story of Jonah: Jonah, the disobedient one, who winds up inside a fish. The fish is longer than a car; it is a monster fish, a leviathan, a whale that takes the prophet in its jaws and swallows him like the walleye has taken Claire's fly. But this Jonah cries out. He doesn't like it in that belly of hell. This Jonah is forgiven. The whale sounds; it leaps and breaches; and in the end, it vomits the boy onto dry land.

* * *

Mick does not tell this story to Claire, because that's not how it happened in real life. Instead he drinks half a Leinie in a hurry and changes the subject. "How much longer do you want to live alone?" he asks. This question has been looming over them for the past twenty-four hours, and Mick is glad when he finally speaks it.

66

Claire fumes and then bursts out, "I'm not giving up my homes! I've been coming here all my life."

Mick is conscious of being in a little boat in bad weather. "Would you let somebody come live with you?"

"Who?" Claire asks with an incredulous look on her face. "You? Jonah?" She grabs another cracker and bites it. "Neither of you are about to give up your lives to live in my house again." Her gaze drops to water level and she focuses intently on the swirls and eddies that pattern the surface.

* * *

"Rise, rise," Mick had called to his brother, all those years ago. He'd sent that line out, put his whole being into it, and watched the surface for a bubble, a ring, or the sign of a great white fish. He'd waited for God to read his brother's heart and save him. But nothing had lured Jonah to the surface. Not even the crows that came, as if pulled out of the sky, to perform their noisy ceremony Three days and three nights passed, and no whale belched his brother onto shore. There was no wet miracle, only a funeral for Jonah, and for Mick, the thrall of memory.

* * *

"My brother's dead," Mick says, suddenly panicked that his mother is expecting Jonah to rise now – a god-man, blue as the cold water, returning from the depths.

Claire pleats and unpleats her upper lip like an accordion, and the shift in gears is almost visible. Her eyes come off the water and pierce her son as she snaps, "Don't you think I know that?"

"A companion...I was talking about someone we'd pay to stay with you."

"I walk three miles a day! Everyday! Why would I let someone in white shoes start wheeling me around?"

"I'm just suggesting someone to keep track of details. More like a secretary."

"Absolutely not. Totally unnecessary. I have a system."

"What kind of system?"

"Notes. I write notes to myself."

67

"What if you forget to look at them?"

Claire's face is pinched and threatening. "If you think I'm going to wander off and get lost, think again." She pauses with a laugh that's loud and alarming. "I've got a dog who knows his way home. And if this is about burning down the house, just pray that I'm in it. When I think I need someone to look after me, I'll call that doctor with the suicide machine."

They spend the next few minutes irate and looking out in opposite directions. "Without memory, there is only blank space," Mick thinks. And then he realizes, without memory, there is no pain. Oblivion is just another method of escape.

It's been a long, in and out day. The sky shows some promise of clearing, and Claire decides it's time for a walk. She puts in at Fox Island.

Mick is again seized by the need to remind his mother of all the rare events in his brother's life. With some trepidation, he asks if she remembers the time Jonah found the double egg clutch. Claire is eager to see if the nest is still there, even though more than thirty years have passed. Mick humors her and follows her lead along the spit of land and into the cedar forest.

As they make their way among the fragrant trees, Claire picks rocks out of circles of moss. Pine needles stitch in and out of low clouds, and mist rises from the ground. The place seems hushed and holy.

Still Mick is amazed when his mother leads him to a tangle of cattail, fern, and twig, contoured to fit a loon's white breast. When he kneels down beside the nest, time slips; memory collapses into the present. He sees the pieces of shell, olive-colored shards with brown speckles, enshrined in the twigs. Here is evidence that something can return or be done again, and in this domain of miracles, Mick sees a way back and a way forward. Annie is the one who comes to mind.

* * *

As Mick and Claire retrace their steps, the sky clears and the sun shines with a passion that comes when the limelight is so hard won. Claire collects rocks full of quartz and mica chips, and before she puts them in the pockets of her hunting jacket, she shows Mick their sparkle. When he asks what they're for, she says she'll edge a new garden with them. By the time they climb back into the boat, her hem droops down to her knees from the weight of the stones. "Don't sink us," Mick jokes as he navigates their way around the lake.

It's after seven, and the loons have begun their evening laughter. Claire ties up to her dock. She pulls the stringer of fish out of the water and passes it reverently to Mick, although later, he assumes, she will squeeze their hearts into their mouths, and Mick will tell himself, as he always has, that fish don't have nerves. Now Claire lingers to watch the sun go down.

Still elated by their find, Mick walks up to the house with the fish. He lays them in the sink and their tails flap and their skins flash like precious metals. He breaks up kindling, and the sound is like the snap of a hypnotist's fingers calling him again into the present.

Mick lights the fire and the house gets smoky. He opens a window and he can see Claire through the bug screen. She is walking slowly down the dock past the red-lettered dates toward the future. Mick stares at the sun until it sinks into the lake.

At the end of the dock, Claire is a blur. She appears to be floating on the seam between the water and the air. And then her arms seem to rise like wings and her head tucks down, and Mick remembers the pockets full of stones. He does not watch any longer. He crashes through the door and down the path.

Claire resembles a black and white bird, flying out over the water. Mick follows her slow motion flight, the lithe form suspended between the heavens and the deep. It hangs there in limbo, for what seems a lifetime, after leaving earth.

Mick runs along the boards that mark out the decades of their lives. He imagines a compressed spirit sinking through the gray water. He imagines his mother flooded with the past, and then the wake of bubbles, like a string of pearls.

But as he nears the end of the dock, things start coming back into focus. He sees clearly that Claire does not need saving. She is sitting in a lawn chair, gazing out into the heart of the lake. There are fishermen trolling in the dusk.

There are scattered wails and tremolos, and a sliver of moon, rising.

Mick stands next to his mother's chair, but she does not seem to hear his fast breath or the roar of his heart. She does not turn, and he is not sure what is gone and what is left, but he is not tempted to measure what he has lost.

He places a hand on Claire's shoulder, and she opens her arms wide to everything that is before her – to the painted sky and the sequined water. And with a look that can only be described as one of rapture, she turns toward Mick as if to say, "*This* is all you need to remember."

IN THE LAST PLACE
Joseph Green

Whatever fits together comes apart.
That's how the retired engineer still looks
at a problem – a frozen bolt, a stuck lock,
a stopped lawnmower – as if some quirk,
some wrinkle of his brain makes him see
any object in its exploded view: the leaky
bucket laid out as rivets, wire, and tin;
the clock as cogs and springs, face and hands.
Politics? money. Love? electricity.
His wife: clipped coupons, fruit in jars.

But something new has gotten into her,
something he can't explain – a dropped
stitch, a boiled egg in a cereal box,
spoiling in a closet, her lost pocketbook
turning up in the oven, the bathroom
cabinet spilling used facial tissues.
She puts her lipstick on to wash the dishes.
He puzzles over the way she's changed
and the way she's stayed the same as she was.

But these are still days of saved pennies,
salvaged parts. Whatever can be dismantled
can be fixed. The answer, he says, is sure to be
something so obvious you just didn't think of it.
Lost things surface in the last place you look.
The clock in the kitchen has always been
electric, time itself running on love
as it does even now on the face of the microwave,
green light-emitting diodes glowing
bright as hope above the stove.

IT'S ONLY MAKE BELIEVE
Barbara Beckman

It was a question my co-worker Marnie and I discussed only once, but I thought about often. Though never stated quite so formally, the question came down to this: When working with people whose minds have been altered by diseases such as Alzheimer's – whose inner lives are far from the here and now – do you enter their world and be the person they want you to be, or do you give them a reality check, tell them you're not their sister, their farmhand, or their customer; tell them they're not in their mother's kitchen, their father's barn, or their family's store. "Do you delight or do you disappoint?" was how Marnie asked it, and when she put it that way, how could you say disappoint?

Our nursing-assistant training course had advised "reality check," a recommendation echoed by higher-ups in Peaceful Valley Nursing Home, where Marnie and I had worked for three years. But in fact the higher-ups were seldom present during the evening and night shift we worked, which is why, I suppose, Marnie set about doing what she believed was best, what she said would bring the most peace to the lives of the residents. "And who," she said, "didn't deserve a little peace when they reached their end on this earth?" But peace through deception? I wasn't sure, but I did know Marnie had a way of saying things that stuck with you.

At least once a week we'd discuss one of Marnie's many anomalous yet believable exchanges with residents, usually over an onion-smothered cheeseburger and a tall beer – our reward for surviving a back-breaker weekend 12-hour shift. That shift paid more than the others, and Marnie and I both needed the money. She was an actress who couldn't get enough work to support herself, and I was a recently married history student trying to pay my way through college. Opposites in aspirations, we were opposites in looks, too. Marnie had spiked hair a half-inch short, dyed dark red. Mine was mouse-brown, pulled back in a ponytail. Back in elementary school, I was the one teachers gladly put in charge if they had to leave the classroom for a moment. Marnie, I imagined, was the one substitute teachers were warned about and student teachers dreaded. Though a friendship between the two of us seemed unlikely, early on we forged one when we agreed on two key points: this wasn't the no-brainer job we expected it would be, and trite as it might sound, we really could make a difference between a resident having a good day or a bad one. And a good day? In Marnie's words, "It was a helluva lot more than a full stomach and dry britches."

* * *

The first time I observed Marnie enter into a resident's world was when Vernon Johnson, a grain farmer for sixty years, couldn't sleep. It was midnight, and wearing his black and red plaid wool jacket over his baby-blue flannel pajamas and his grass-green Farmer's Union cap tipped crooked on his bald head, he paced the hall with his walker, mumbling and occasionally hollering.

"How about some ice cream?" I asked, relying on the distraction that worked with many residents, but Marnie had a different idea. Like a compassionate counselor, she calmly asked Vernon what was wrong, then listened carefully as he explained. It took several broken sentences and much repetition, but finally the problem became evident: Vernon didn't have enough money to get the second house moved off the farm, and he needed that land for his crop.

A reality check, I thought, Vernon needs a reality check. "Vernon, you're at..." I started, but before I could finish, Marnie jumped in.

"Mr. Johnson, my name is Miss Carlstad and I can certainly help you with that," she said, her voice taking a professionally authoritative turn. "I just came on board here at the bank a few weeks ago, and I work in the...farm-lending department." Swiftly, decisively, she put her hand out and he took it, shaking it firmly as if they might one day be the best of business partners. Under her arm she carried a notebook she'd grabbed from the nurses' station. I was quite certain she didn't know the first thing about farms or banks, but she held Vernon's attention. What did he see when he looked at her? A banker wearing a pinstripe business suit, or a nursing assistant dressed in regulation blues set off by a multicolored scarf wrapped around her head like a turban? The nursing home's dress code didn't address turbans, but based on what it said about socks (white only), jewelry (nothing that hangs) and bras (required), I was pretty sure they'd be frowned upon.

"I don't think I've seen you here before," Vernon said. "Usually I work with Phil. Where's Phil?"

"Phil's on vacation, but he thoroughly apprised me of your situation before he left."

Another resident's call light flashed and I had to go. Oh, how I hated to leave that scene – Marnie with her arm around Vernon's shoulders as if they were old chums, leading him toward a table with two chairs and offering him a cup of coffee. On my way down the hall, I wondered – was she using Vernon to practice her theater skills, or was she really helping him? Ultimately, would she delight or disappoint?

I knew when I returned that she had indeed delighted him. Cap off, legs crossed, spit flying, eyes sparkling, eighty-eight-year-old Vernon sipped coffee from a Styrofoam cup, bragging about the new equipment he hoped to purchase next year and how pleased he was to have some additional land. She'd given him an outstanding deal and he couldn't thank her enough – a no-interest loan and no payback until the land started producing. "How come Phil never gave me that kind of deal," Vernon asked. He went to bed smiling and slept the rest of the night.

That was the first of several exchanges I observed between Marnie and residents, not all of them quite so fun. Residents dying, for example. But even then Marnie had her role to play. In their last days, even last hours, it wasn't unusual for dying residents to fade in and out, to experience people from their past threading in and out of their consciousness. "Mama, are you there?" they'd cry out. "Mama, is that you?" I wouldn't know what to say, and more than anything I wanted to escape the room, but not Marnie. She'd go to their bedsides and hold their limp hands or stroke their ashen faces. In a voice that could erase the worst nightmare, she'd say, "Don't worry, I'm right here," sometimes adding endearments like "honey" or "dear." As if they'd been given a tranquilizer, they'd stop their struggling and their wrinkled, frowning faces would settle into calm.

Sometimes she did even more. Every once in a while, at the end of a resident's life, trouble that had been suppressed for years came rumbling to the surface, revealing itself in broken utterances that only Marnie took the time to understand. She would listen, figure out what was needed, then grant it. Marnie became the child who apologized, the wife who forgave, the friend who returned.

* * *

"I don't think I've seen you here before," said the white-haired man with no legs who was propped in the wheelchair to my right. He had a husky, strong voice and was able to feed himself, unlike Paul, who was to my left. Paul was the reason I was assigned to this particular table.

"Usually I'm on third floor, but tonight they put me on second," I told him.

"Glad you came by," he said. "It's good to see a new face." His hospitality took me off guard, prompting me to wonder what kind of mental problem landed him on this unit.

"Frank, stop your flirting and eat your lasagna," hollered another nursing assistant from a table behind us.

"Goddamned waitresses should mind their own business," Frank leaned over and told me. His mental problem became a little clearer. I imagined Frank might be one of those residents who would leave a quarter on the table as a tip. We had a few of those upstairs. Marnie was the only one who would take the tips, and while the residents were sleeping, she would return them to their pockets or their purses. The rest of us followed the rules, taking the tips and giving them to the nurse-in-charge. Marnie said she didn't trust that system.

Paul, the resident I was feeding, ate baby-sized bites, and I could tell it would take a while for him to drink his thickened milk and eat his pureed lasagna, peas, and peaches. But I didn't mind because Frank intrigued me.

"I don't believe I've ever seen one of these," Frank said, holding up his breadstick by one end, smirking. He had the look of someone who'd just thought of a dirty joke, but debated whether to share it. He tore it in half and took a bite.

"How is it?" I asked. He raised his eyebrows twice, then winked. I braced myself for the wisecrack, but instead there was silence, followed by stuttering. He couldn't find the word, which wasn't unusual for any of the residents, but somehow it surprised me with Frank. Finally he settled on one: quiet.

"Frank, you better start on that lasagna," hollered the same nursing assistant who had hollered the first time.

"Goddamned waitress can't keep her mouth shut."

"Would you like something to drink?" I asked, handing Frank his glass of apple juice.

"No, no," he said, "especially not that. I quit drinking forty years ago, but that doesn't stop me from pouring 'em and serving 'em." A bartender. Frank had been a bartender and he thought I was offering him a beer. It was at this point that Marnie would have started talking to him as if she were a customer, asking him about drinks, talking about sports, entering his world, but not just entering, promoting. I wasn't ready for that, yet I did want to visit because I liked Frank's style. I liked his indirect way of getting information, which was so typical of a bartender. Wanting to know, but not wanting to intrude.

"How do you like it here?" I said, wondering how he'd interpret "here."

"The Comstock? It's the best place I've ever worked," he said. "The customers are good and except for that big-mouth back there, the waitresses aren't bad either."

Paul stopped eating and his face turned red. I'd worked in the nursing home long enough to know this was not a good sign. The smell wafted up, and Frank knew, too.

"Close the door to the goddamned can," he hollered. "And turn up that jukebox." I went to the boom box on top of the piano and increased the volume. A country-classics station played It's Only Make Believe, and Frank hummed along.

"That song was popular when I graduated in thirty-eight, but I don't suppose you were around then," he said. In bartender style, Frank was trying to find out how old I was.

"Did you fight in the 'Big One?'" I asked, reminding myself of Marnie. How many times had I heard her talk about the "Big One," never calling it World War II, because she said that's not how the old men knew it.

The puzzled look again, then Frank answered, "Quebec."

The stench got stronger, and Frank announced, "Closing time, time to go home." I wheeled him back to his room, which looked like every other – a single bed with side-rails, a chest of drawers, side-table with towels and disposable briefs set on top for bedtime. Without the music, without the mouthy waitress, without the conversation, where would Frank think he was, and who would I be? I knew a reality check was the right thing, but I didn't want to be the one to disappoint.

"Glad to have met you," Frank said. He extended his hand and I stood there, arms glued to my side, not sure what to do. "You be sure to stop in next time you're in town...and have one on me." Still hesitant, I took his hand. Feeling its warmth, the strength of the grip, I couldn't help but shake it. "Good night," I said, and left the room. Frank resumed humming the chorus to the song he'd heard in the dining room. When I reached the door, I turned around once more. With a dry washcloth, Frank was wiping the already-clean tray table that locked him in his wheelchair. Wiping away the eternal ring left by the sweaty beer bottle of a long departed – or just departed – customer.

Author's Note: I've worked in the same nursing home for over twelve years, primarily in the Alzheimer's Unit. With regard to orienting residents to reality, this depends in large part on the personality of the nursing assistant. Where I work, the nursing assistants tend to go along with whatever world the resident happens to be in at the time, trying not to upset him or her, but rather offering comfort. This seems a very humane approach. In the past, prior to the development of separate Alzheimer's units, one approach applied to all and that approach was orienting the residents to reality, often with upsetting results.

SPANISH ENTERS THE ROOM
Joe Milosch

Spanish enters the room like a flock of red-hooded finches
perching first on TV antennas, then on the pictures
of Cesar Chavez, family, and the bride and groom
outside the Santa Dominga church.

In the picture, the couple's eyes
are like freshly turned fields of
onion, tomato, and carrot farms,
snug in the county of string ties.

In the kitchen, the women chop ham hocks,
clean cilantro, and their conversation takes wing,
circling above their heads like a sunlit ring,
before it enters the living room like a flock of red-capped
finches that perches among the thickets of Jimmie's ears.

On TV, the Forty-Niners run up the score
on the Giants, who are as helpless as Jimmie,
sitting in the wheelchair beside me.

Ninety-nine pounds of flesh hides the suffering man.
He has come to this: tied to his chair by tape around his
wrists, covered by a rainbow blanket,
outlining the bones protruding from his legs and hips.

Are the women singing a hymn
as they make menudo and beer ices
in the Frigidaire? Whatever they do,
it is for him, and the memory of him
eating a late breakfast with a beer as he watches the game.

Jimmie's eyes are like two clumps of soil
kicked aside by a plow in the field.
In the winter he pruned apricot and plum trees,
and in the summer he picked oranges until
he could no longer remember which side
of the ladder to climb, and then
he became angry out of fear and pride.

Lorna says, *I won't put him in a home.*
He won't know anybody. They won't know
his favorite radio station or TV show,
or how to make his eggs with a little Tabasco.
There he'll die a hungry, lonely stranger.
Here he'll die mi esposo.

Lorna enters the living room,
A cuanto va San Francisco? she asks,
and waits for the score to flash on the screen.
She rubs his hair as if offering a prayer
that her belief in the afterlife will give him a future.

San Francisco is winning, she tells Jimmie,
kissing him lightly on the ear
and whispering, *Que bueno.*

She has told me of their life:
how she brought him lunch and helped him prune.
Now their life goes beyond the weighing
of words, none of which express
the loneliness of her work and sleep.

As she is about to leave, she tells me
Jimmie was a good worker.
Smart too.

The look on her face demands shouting,
demands that I see how Jimmie
used both hands at the same time
to pick and bag the fruit without bruising it.

And if that wasn't possible,

show him walking in his own footsteps
between rows of cotton.

And if that wasn't possible,

show how the tomatoes he picked became as smooth
as identical thoughts in their crate.

And if that wasn't possible,

let Jimmie do something crazy like dance
a Cebraditas around a warming fire with a pint
and a handkerchief in his hip pocket.

And if that wasn't possible,

let a crowd of field hands surround
Jimmie in a dance, chanting ritual songs that
celebrate the passing of manhood.

And if that wasn't possible,

to see the love and respect she carries in the lines
around her eyes.

And if that wasn't possible,

to call Jimmie by his proper name.

And if that wasn't possible,

let Jimmie be himself again
before disease consumed his brain
with snail-like precision.

As Lorna leaves the room,
she leaves in the green plush carpet
only her heel print to bear witness
to the look in her eyes.

Jimmie faces the screen.
His eyes have not moved all morning.
Sometimes his facial muscles twitch,
making him seem to frown.

We pray that his mind doesn't toil
behind the closed doors of the shed of his body,
that his mind soars like flames in a brush pile,
that under the clouds of his eyes,
he wanders fields in November with his breath
seen in the rain as he clips and ties
the finger-thick branches.

He no longer gives signs of recognition or love,
but he lives. He lives somewhere between
the odors of tripe, beef feet, pig feet, hominy,
the announcer's play by play, and the smell of coffee
perking through a layer of cinnamon sticks.

He lives surrounded by the sounds of his language,
which are finches riding the air currents,
landing to scratch for food.

Listen!
How their beaks click
as they crack small syllabic seeds.

CALLE ESPAÑA
Eduardo A. Alvarez, M.D.

In my native town, a sleepy, peaceful place, nothing ever happened but what had happened before. Since I was a young boy, however, just turned five, the world was still a new place for me. In those times, it was the custom for entire families to be found in one part of town. Often they were identified by the street where they lived. Townspeople spoke of the Pichardos on the 17th of February Street, the Pereiras on the Avenida Colon, and the Alvarez on Calle España. In these family enclaves, everyone was treated with much affection and respect.

My mother had a first cousin who lived in our neighborhood. He was a kind man, pleasant and courteous, and very good-looking. No one ever spoke of his wife, who lived secluded and never took part in the family get-togethers. I had never seen her, and for a long time I assumed that she lived in another part of the country.

One day towards the end of my fifth year, I ventured through the courtyard door of our neighbor's house. The interior was a rather large patio, bordered on one side by the house, and on three other sides by high walls. At the back of the patio sat a lady, strong and tall – to me, she appeared to be a giant – very pale and blonde. She looked like a character from one of the storybooks my mother had been reading to me. All around her were birds, some in cages and some flying free, parrots, magpies, parakeets, nightingales, canaries, and crows. I stood still, curious, but not afraid, admiring everything.

The lady signaled to me to come closer and very amiably showed me all her birds and a little monkey that she had tied to a tree with a long narrow chain. She seemed tranquil and happy. I had a pleasant time in her company, and later she showed me out very courteously. She invited me to come again, and this I did. I visited her often, and in spite of the isolation in which she was used to living, she received me with evident pleasure.

But as time went on, I noticed certain alarming changes in her behavior. The greetings she gave me were now brusque. Sometimes they were delivered in a hoarse, faltering voice, sometimes in creature-like grunts. She still allowed me to walk around her patio and watch her birds, but now she remained seated in her isolated corner. I grew curious and wanted to know more about her, but no one in the neighborhood would ever speak about her, at least not in my presence. Everyone seemed to accept her isolation and strangeness without comment.

This lady, I found out, was the wife of my mother's cousin. Her name was Dona Anita, and although my uncle still spoke distantly of having a wife, Dona Anita's own family seemed to have forgotten she existed. Her sister Lola lived next door, but they never exchanged greetings. In fact, the pair of sisters was study in opposites. Whereas we referred to Dona Anita formally as "Dona," Lola was plain "Lola," a nickname. (No one knew her real name.) Her doors were always open, and we boys in the neighborhood would go in and out of her house without her ever complaining. On the contrary, she seemed eager to show how different she was from her sister. Even physically, Lola looked like Dona Anita's opposite: dark, stocky, and quick to smile, with dark, expressive eyes. She was not pretty, but she was always in a good mood and ready to please. She had many cats, but no birds.

As I mentioned, with time, Dona Anita became more reserved with me, just as she had always been with other people. Being still very young, I couldn't understand why she should change towards me. Each time, her patio seemed less of a paradise. My visits became more and more infrequent. Many times she was upset and irritable, and whenever this would happen, I would make a quick escape.

One day I entered the patio and she wasn't in her usual corner. I heard shouting from a room nearby and I recognized her voice. She was calling her husband's name, over and over, and talking incoherently. I was afraid she was being hurt by someone, and I ran to her aid.

What I saw, nothing in my life had prepared me for. Through the open door of her room I could make out an old woman, naked, her clothing torn off, her skin hanging loosely on her bones. She was soiled and foul-smelling, and her white hair was disheveled. She looked at me without seeing me. She did not speak to me, and after a moment of studying me, she continued her screaming. I turned on my heels and ran out of the door of her courtyard and never again ventured inside. My sadness knew no limits. I wanted to erase her from my memory, but still, sixty-five years later, I remember with clarity her strong figure, her birds, her little monkey doing pirouettes, and all the changes that followed.

Ten years later she was dead, but what should happen? Her sister Lola began to close her doors. Her cats, who had never before been allowed out, could be seen running in the streets, as if escaping, disoriented, unable to understand the dramatic change in their mistress. Within the year, Lola was also dead. I don't remember if there was a funeral.

I do remember my final interview with her, as disconcerting as the one I'd had with her sister Dona Anita. I was older now, fifteen, and a young man on his way to the university in the capital to study medicine. I was saying my good-byes to everyone in the neighborhood, and I thought I'd pay a call on Lola. I knocked at her door and the maid answered, but the young girl merely shook her head when I asked if Lola could see me. No, her mistress was not receiving any callers.

I was about to turn to go, when from the corner of my eye, I caught sight of her, Dona Anita's sister, Lola. An old, white-haired woman came racing out of a back room toward the door. Her eyes had a wild look, her white hair was disheveled, and her clothes hung in tatters on her gaunt, soiled body. She too looked at me without a glimmer of recognition. Then she lunged forward as if she were one of her cats wanting to escape. Quickly, the maid slammed the door in my face. I stood still, shocked, listening to the old woman's screams of protest on the other side of the door.

Then slowly, as if the ten years that had intervened since I had last seen Dona Anita were catching up with me, I made my way down the steps of that house and onto Calle España Street. I felt suddenly very old. There was nothing here to surprise me anymore. I was ready and relieved to be leaving home.

VISITATIONS: PERU
Elisavietta Ritchie

By day he sleeps on the flat high-walled roof
beneath the shelter of tin. Hot. No rain here.
Dawn and dusk when he howls for stew
or fish from the river of childhood,
wine from the cafes of his youth,
two grown-ups fasten the ladder,
unbar the trap door,
bring rice and beans, or bread.
He eats with his fingers.
Someone rinses his beard in a gourd
which he tries to drink from while they
lower and dump the old pail.
Up there it stinks.
No one goes up there alone.
We are not allowed.

Juan Pedro at school also has
an uncle up on his roof he has never seen.
Certain nights while my sister and I
lie in our little high room
our uncle somehow climbs down,
crawls in our window.
Those nights the moon's full.
Eyes gleam through his hair.
We huddle, pretending to sleep
while he circles our mattress three times.
Then he returns to the roof.
We never speak of his visits.
In a few years my sister will cook
his beans and rice, bake his bread.
I will carry them up to the roof.

THAT'S WHAT IT'S ALL ABOUT
Sue Mayfield-Geiger

I look at his trembling hands and realize he is cold, so I grab a blanket off a nearby chair and wrap it around his shoulders. He smiles. We've been waiting for over an hour. First in the waiting area, and now in the cubbyhole examining room. He seems uncomfortable.

"Are you warmer now, Dad?" I ask him. He just looks at me for a while, and then he says in a raspy voice, "I guess." He is slumped over, looking at the floor. He is not my father. He is not the robust man who used to hoist me up in the air and carry me over his shoulders. He does not possess the muscular body my mother fell in love with in 1937. He has lost the twinkle that used to live in his beautiful gray eyes. His once full face is now painfully thin with bony cheekbones sticking out like two doorknobs. His expression is blank. I gaze toward his hands, clasped together in his lap, holding onto the blanket for dear life. The skin on his hands is scaly; they are not the manly hands that sanded wood, played golf, strummed a guitar, fingered a piano scale, or touched my mother's hair. I want to scream, "Get out of my father's body, you monster!" But I know it won't do any good. I know that the monster is winning the battle and I am helpless. Maybe this new doctor will have some answers; maybe a new drug is on the horizon.

"Why are we here?" he asks.

"To see a new doctor," I reply.

"Oh," he says.

His spunky spirit is waning. In the early stages, he was so feisty. He used to talk incessantly, ranting and raving, proclaiming that there wasn't a goddamned thing wrong with him and that just because he couldn't remember who the President of the United States was, or what day it was, or what year it was, didn't make him crazy. "I'm just getting old," he'd say. "Everyone who gets old loses their memory from time to time." But it was more than that. He couldn't remember how to get home from the grocery store any more. He was starting to ask my mother who she was. He imagined things. "Who are those people sitting over there on the sofa? Someone broke into the house and stole all my money! Whose house is this?" And so on.

But now going into the third year, he was becoming less verbal. His short-term memory was just about gone, but his long-term memory was pretty much intact. "I see my mother," he'd say. "She's lying on her bed with her long hair draped over her pillow. I'm sitting on the edge of the bed and she has her hand on my arm. She's smiling."

Dad's mother died when he was seven, and he often reenacts this scene, because she died in front of his very eyes. "She'd been sick in bed for so long," he would recall. "One day I walked over to her bed and told her I was going out to play, but that I'd be back. Then she raised her head off the pillow, took a deep breath, like this (he would always show you), then she fell back and she died." Tears would well up in his eyes and he would sob with such emotion, that everyone around him would sob too. It all seemed like yesterday to him.

"It shouldn't be too much longer, Dad," I tell him. He's getting irritated. "I'm hungry," he states. Now I'm seething. "These damn doctors. Why do they overbook like this and make us wait?" I need to entertain him, but with what. He starts to remove the blanket. His hands are reaching out like he's trying to grab something. I have to think fast. "Hey, Dad, remember this?" I back up and begin my act.

"You put your right hand out, you put your right hand in, you put your right hand out, and then you shake it all about. You do the Hokey-Pokey, and you turn yourself around. That's what it's all about." I'm singing with vigor, moving body parts, and I've got his attention. Good. I continue. "You put your left hand out...." And so it goes until I've gone through about fourteen body parts. Dad is watching me intently, still clutching the blanket. I've become his personal T.V. set. His eyes are fixed on my every move. At one point, he mouths ever so softy, "That's what it's all about."

"Right, Dad!" I scream. "That's it. You remember!"

So, now I'm starting over; I think I'm on the butt part. "You put your backside out, you put your backside in, you

87

put your backside out, and you shake it all about. You do the Hokey-Pokey, and you turn yourself around..." I turn myself around into the watchful stare of the doctor who has just entered the room.

I am sure he is wondering which one of us is the patient, the stone-faced, elderly gentleman sitting on the edge of the examining table wrapped like an Indian or the middle-aged dancing fool gyrating and singing loudly.

"Oh, hi," I say much too shrilly. "Just entertaining my Dad while we wait. You remember the Hokey-Pokey, don't you?" Of course, he doesn't. He's from Columbia, and his thick accent tells me that he's not sure what to do at this juncture. Finally, he gets the picture and starts to ask Dad the routine questions.

"Look," I say. "Please don't put him through all that. I'm just here to get another opinion. We're thinking we may have to go the nursing home route, and I just wanted to get some suggestions from you." The doctor seems okay, but still not the knight in shining armor I've been looking for. He tells me that I need to be realistic. I need to prepare myself, as does my mother, and that we may have to eventually consider a feeding tube, and on and on and on. I know within minutes that this guy is not going to give me any new answers. He finishes the exam and shakes my hand. "Let me know if I can do anything else," he says before he departs. Like, what else is there? You tell me. You went to medical school. Can't you figure this out?

I look back over at Dad. He's still holding on tight to the blanket. I continue, "You put your whole self out, you put your whole self in, you put your whole self out, and you shake it all about. You do the Hokey-Pokey, and you turn yourself around. That's what it's all about."

THE SAME RAIN
Norma Fain Pratt

Warsaw, 1922

Esther looks just like her mother, Feyge. Both women have small, hooked noses and fierce, ice blue eyes. There is a wide space between their front teeth that they tease each other about:

"Ester'l, can you whistle?" Feyge asks her daughter.

"Mamenu," Esther answers, "Sure, but you first."

Their bodies are similarly compact, short, and muscular, except the buttocks slope and each woman laments a roundish belly that hints at possible pregnancy or merely suggests poor posture.

That's where the resemblance ends. Esther appears quiet, almost withdrawn, except that once in a while a wide range of emotions plays across her face as if escaping against her will. Feyge, who always seemed old before her time, has a resigned anxiety about her and a fiery fly-off-the-handle sharp tongue that constantly offends her daughter.

Especially when Esther is seventeen and Feyge is forty-five, Feyge's no-matter-what, you name it, drives Esther crazy. And Esther keeps an ever-expanding list of her mother's shortcomings:

- Mama still wears an old fashioned wig, the *shaytl.*
- Mama prays like a man, three times a day. Twice a day she goes to the *shul* (the synagogue), once in the pre-dawn and then at dusk.
- Mama refuses to learn to read or write in Yiddish or Polish. She's illiterate.
- Mama's voice is harsh and unpleasant when she sells vegetables in the market.
- Mama never lets Papa kiss her and she insults him in front of all of us – all ten of us children.

89

- Mama knows nothing about politics, neither Poale Zionism nor Socialist Bundism, nothing, only the price of chicken, the ripeness of apples, and old-fashioned remedies for headaches.

Esther even has on the list what she recently overheard her mother telling the *mazinkele*, the youngest member of the family, her ten-year-old sister Zelde: "When it rains here in Warsaw, it rains everywhere in the world. It's the same rain everywhere." Although Esther herself is far from being an educated person, having barely completed three full formal years in a state-run Yiddish school for girls, she knows this is a very big world at least thousands of miles in circumference. There are continents, oceans, islands, mountains, and many different climates. What kind of dismal ignorance believes it rains everywhere when it rains here in cloudy, gray Warsaw? In *Eretz Yisroel*, Palestine, it hardly ever rains. Esther's Zionist friends reassure her about that. And, in the *goldene medina*, the golden land, it rains a lot in New York, but very little out West, in the land of Indians and the gold rush. There it is a desert like Palestine.

Esther listens very carefully to weather reports because she has decided to marry Itzik and get out of rainy Warsaw. To go somewhere away from the two crowded rooms on the third floor; away from Feyge's sharp tongue; away from the endless washing for thirteen people; away from the vegetable market where she helps Feyge sell the greens for soups, the parsley, the celery, the parsnips, every morning from dawn to noon; away from the anti-Semites. So what if Itzik isn't so handsome, if his ears stick out like a donkey's as her older sister Lena once said. So what if he doesn't have a trade exactly. We are young, strong, and healthy. Not like Mama who lives in her cocoon, waiting for the *Meshiakh* (Messiah) to come on a horse led by the prophet Eliahu. Itzik loves her like no other boy has ever loved her.

Even Papa hardly pays any attention to her. Maybe because he is so tired of girls. She's the next to the youngest of ten daughters. She often compares herself to her one brother and her nine sisters: I'm not as smart as my brother Hershel, who moved to "The Bronx" in America, or as beautiful as Malka. I'm not as funny as little Zelda, as good a cook as Rena, as refined as Miriam, as studious as Anna, as careful with money as Celia, as compassionate as

Brindl or as cheerful and witty as Brokhe and Lena. Not long ago Papa called her *fire bren* (burning fire) and then he called her *vilde khaye* (wild animal) which was absolutely not a compliment. She hates to read distrust of her in his eyes because she loves him more than anyone else in the family – papa with his mellow gentle brown eyes, his graying hair and his slight lisp after a glass of shabbos wine. He is twenty years older than Mama.

Itzik pays attention to her, really pays attention. He comes to their market stall everyday around ten o'clock after he helps his father unload the kitchenware they sell on the other side of the market. Sometimes he brings a flower, sometimes a sweet or a glass of tea for Feyge. "For Mama," he says.

He stands beside Esther, not even looking into her face, and she can feel his powerful love for her coming out of him in great, warm, delicious waves.

Mama feels the waves too. "Go work," she says to Itzik. "What are you? A loafer with nothing to do but hang around the women?" Itzik, his donkey ears reddening, looks at her out of the corner of his eye. Then he turns to her, slowly, elaborately, elegantly, without a hint of sarcasm, saying: "Mama, I want to thank you for allowing me to stay here with yourself and my beloved Esther. You know I want to marry her. I want to give her a good life. I want to support her. She says she loves me too. We are ready for a wedding."

Once Feyge started chopping the wilted parsley from two days ago, not looking at either of them. Her lips tight, almost white with a worried little anger. "My daughter is too young to marry. You, Itzik, are also only eighteen. Wait. What's the hurry? I married at fourteen. Look what it's brought me." At that she broke out into a funny cackle. A bitter cackle that made Esther put that "cackle" on the top of her "What I Don't Like About Mama" list.

Sometimes in the evening when little Zelda is sleeping and Papa is out visiting his family, Esther tries to broach the subject of a wedding including just the immediate family.

"That means your eight married sisters and their husbands, my three brothers, their wives, the cousins, maybe fifty, sixty people. Papa's two sisters and his seven nieces. Plus, you are too young."

"We can go to the Rabbi's house. Just you, Papa, and Itzik's parents and two witnesses."

"Are you crazy?" Feyge winces. "Maybe we can have the wedding in the butcher shop?"

The butcher shop stops Esther cold. She knows Mama is again, for the millionth time, just being thoughtlessly cruel. She imagines in disgust her wedding canope, the *khupe*, touching a leg of lamb. She feels nauseous.

Esther cries out to her mother, "Mama, you'll say any stupid thing to stop me, won't you?" her face contorted in a grimace.

But Feyge turns away from her daughter.

"Fe, such a face," she says in disgust.

Esther meets Itzik most evenings at around eight o'clock behind the old synagogue on Nvostik Street. They sit on the rock just behind the grille entrance to the building so no one can see them from the street. A deep shadow always falls on the rock, summer or winter, making them invisible.

"She still says no," Esther moans.

"Then ask your father," he suggests in a loud voice.

"My father's word does not count in our house. Papa is afraid of her sharp tongue. He says, "Feyge, you are sticking needles into me with what you are saying.""

"Saying, saying," Itzik repeats. "Can you imagine a whole family being afraid of what one woman says?"

Esther kisses him and slides her tongue into his mouth.

"We'll have to go to *Eretz Yisroel* with the next group and get married there – with our friends," he whispers, blowing a tiny feather off her bangs with the softest breath. It tickles her and she shivers while thinking, "If I become pregnant that would force Mama's hand."

The letter from her brother Hershel in The Bronx, Tremont Avenue, America arrives on a Monday morning. It is dated August 14, 1922, two months earlier. Everyone is at home when Papa opens it and the four tickets fall on the floor. Big, colorful tickets, second-class to New York City.

"New York City's somewhere near The Bronx," Papa explains. Who would go? Mama and Papa and the two youngest daughters, unmarried Esther and little Zelda? That's what everyone thinks at the beginning. It's the obvious choice. But then Papa says he has his two sisters to watch out for.

They aren't well and he can't go to America and leave them like this. Then it surfaces that he had a bad fight with Hershel before his only son left for The Bronx five years ago. He really doesn't want to be dependent on him in a strange land. Mama cries when Papa says he can't get along with Hershel.

"Then I'll go alone and take Brokhe, Lena, and little Zelda," she says defiantly. Esther is shocked. Mama wants to take her two older daughters, both of whom are married but childless, and not Esther. She waits breathlessly for her mother to say something about what will happen to her.

She hopes Mama will say, "Esther is going to marry Itzik and they are going to *Eretz Yisroel*. That's why she's not coming with us to The Bronx."

But Feyge never says it. She remains totally silent about Esther's future. Two weeks before they leave for New York Feyge tells Esther: "Your older sisters are coming with me because they are old enough to find work in New York, and I can trust them to go around in a strange world. You stay with your sister Malka. They need somebody to take care of their three little boys. And Papa will be here and everyone else."

Suddenly, like steam escaping from a boiling, plugged-up teapot, Esther screams: "I hate you, Mama. I'm going to marry Itzik. I don't care what you tell me. When you're gone, I'll marry him."

"I told Malke to watch you. You'll do what she says. When we get enough money for your ticket, we'll send it and you'll come to us. Forget that Itzik. He's a nothing."

Esther has already moved into Malke's tiny apartment when the traveling party leaves for the Hamburg port early in the morning on December 27. She intends to go to the train station to see them off, but instead, she wanders into a small coffee house and sits for several hours drinking hot tea with strong lemon and sugar. Her heart aches, her brain feels like mashed potatoes, and her vision blurs when she stands up at noon to go back to Malke's. She knows the train is long gone. She doesn't even want to see Itzik, who will be waiting for her at the synagogue at eight tonight.

Haifa, 1948

Itzik and Esther are living in Haifa, *Eretz Yisroel* when they receive their American tourist visas. The letter with the stamp from Washington, D.C. came to Khaye, their twenty-year-old daughter, the kibbutznik, who lives near the Golan Heights. When she comes to their small apartment in Haifa for her bi-monthly visit, Khaye brings the letter with her.

Now Itzik is writing one of his interminably long, affectionate, and unpunctuated Yiddish letters to the family in New York, but this time, for a change, he has something exciting to report, because they have finally saved enough money for two tickets on a small ship sailing to New York:

> *dear beloved mama hershel and his wife anna and children brokhe and her children and her husband yankele lena and her children and her husband abie and zelde and her children and her husband carl may everyone be healthy and lucky and may g-d bless the whole family finally we saved enough money for two tickets on a small ship leaving haifa for southern italy and from there to new york a three week voyage to america to return the same way two weeks later we worry about our seven diamonds but they are now big girls and their brother chaim will keep an eye over them so we are not too worried the war is over and this is the time to come to america and see you our beloved family our mama our sisters and their husbands and their children we can never thank you enough for all the packages you sent to us before the war in europe with american canned food with beautiful clothes we lived from your generosity our hearts were torn with such long separation my esther cries every night for her mama and her sisters and brother and she cries for her father may he rest in peace we still pray every night that the sisters and their children in warsaw will be found and we will all have a reunion it is more than time overdue esther and i will arrive in new york at 11 a.m. on august 6 regards to mama to everyone one of you we and our children thank you for all your goodness and we thank*

g-d that he has given us life your beloved son in law and brother in law itzik and your beloved daughter and sister esther.

Esther is still undecided whether she really wants to go to The Bronx on this once-in-a-lifetime trip. True it would be wonderful to see everyone again and all their children, whom she has seen only in baby photographs. They go with their own money, now that Itzik's kitchenware shop is making a living. But will they know her after such a long time? Mama never wrote to her. She can't write. Would Mama remember her disobedient daughter, the one who wouldn't come to The Bronx when they sent the ticket? The daughter who married Itzik without Mama's permission and then ran away to the Holy Land in 1937? It is true, as Itzik says in his letter, that Esther cries at night. But her reason for crying is not for love, not exactly. She feels anger, and it is an old anger over her mother's neglect and meanness. It is also anger about her fear and unresolved longing.

"Maybe, Itzik, we should wait a few more years," she says.

"Maybe, you should make up with your Mama. She wants you to come to see her before she dies. She's over seventy already."

"How do you know she wants to make up? We have never heard a word from her. And, anyway, what's to make up? Water under the bridge," Esther snaps back.

"We have seven beautiful children. You know what *nakhos* that is to her?" Itzik says softly as if he were patting a skittish animal.

"I know Hershel wrote me years ago that I am having too many children. It's old-fashioned. In America everyone has one, maybe two children. What do I need with so many mouths to feed, they asked? Especially since the family is helping us."

"I told Hershel that the children were our diamonds, remember. It is nothing to be ashamed of. Esther, open your heart. I want to see your family, our family," he says putting his arm around her broad shoulders and then kissing her on the cheek.

Esther pushes him away.

95

"Go, write Hershel the truth. Write him that the money they sent was never enough. That they were safe in America and we were always in danger. That it hurts me so much." Esther begins to sob so hard that gigantic, glistening tears run in torrents down her cheeks.

The Bronx, August 1948

The days from Naples to Manhattan on the S.S. Garibaldi give Esther long hours to think about what she wants to do in New York. Everyone wants her to buy them something. They ask her to bring back a refrigerator, a radio, gloves, a collar for Tanya the dog, nylons, chocolate, an endless list that might take years to shop for. Her mind glides away from the list of things to imagining the family in The Bronx. Over and over again, she visualizes how they will be waiting at the pier, standing together like a clump of trees. They'll be waving their hands. The little nieces and nephews, who look just like her own children, will be jumping up and down. Maybe even waving American flags. Mama's face comes into focus. What is her expression? What will her eyes say when we first catch sight of each other?

Just past noon, the ship moves slowly up to the pier. Esther and Itzik stand at the railing. She is looking for that clump of trees. Here and there a few people stand together, but they are not her family. Then she sees a man who looks like her brother Hershel, at least like the picture he recently sent her. He is alone, no Mama, nobody else. How can that be?

As she comes down the gangplank, Hershel moves toward her, but he doesn't embrace her.

"Are you Esther?" he asks politely.

"Yes," she says and starts crying, clinging to Itzik.

"I think you are more beautiful than your picture," he says, showing her the recent picture that she sent to him.

"A funny looking woman," Itzik says.

Esther and Hershel both start laughing.

"Where's Mama and everybody else?" Esther whispers.

"Oh, they're waiting for us at their apartment on the Grand Concourse. They live in a fancy neighborhood. Not like me, a workingman in the East Bronx near the Zoo."

"How far from your house is the Grand Concourse?" Esther asks, feeling an insult churning at the pit of her stomach.

"It's less than an hour by the elevated train from where I live on 177th Street and Tremont Avenue. But I have my business tomorrow. You'll come home with me, rest up a day, and we'll take the train on Saturday morning."

"I want to go to the Grand Concourse now," she says, looking at Itzik who has been standing behind her. He has not even introduced himself to Hershel yet.

"How old are you?" her brother asks.

"I'll be forty-three in September," she replies.

Shaking his head, Hershel mumbles: "You still look like a teenager."

* * *

The two men in the kitchen are talking in hushed voices when Esther wakes up in the tiny bedroom from what seems to her an eternal sleep. It might be early afternoon, because the shadows on the fire escape are quite long. A slight breeze moves the curtains although the famous New York summer muggy humidity weighs her down. Even her hair feels heavy.

Esther catches sight of a picture of her sister Malka and the boys on Hershel's dresser. The lost, the *kaddushim.* Murdered by the Nazis. Long shadows. It must have been taken in 1935 because that's the year she, Itzik, and their four little children left Warsaw for *Eretz Yisroel,* and she gave Malka her heavy winter coat. Malka is wearing that coat in the picture. Beautiful Malka, looking so good even in that klutzy coat. There's Sammy sticking out his tongue. "I hated that child," Esther remembers. And Isaac – the two boys were inseparable.

Esther takes the photograph off the dresser and holds it up to the light. Where is Simon, the eldest? He's missing from the picture. He must have been in school. Yes, he was living with Tante Elsie in Cracow in 1935 and going to the gymnasium. Simon could tell a good joke; he was a smart boy.

On the dresser there are other photographs of people she can barely recognize, at various ages, in various places. Were these the ones who died in the camps, or were they the ones who came to The Bronx? The framed pictures glow in the dusty sunlight, and the dresser seems like an ancestral shrine.

"Some are here and some are gone," she hums to herself.

"Excuse the dust, Esther. My wife's been in the country, in the Catskills, near Liberty all summer," Hershel says coming into his bedroom on tiptoes and seeing her staring at the dresser.

"Oh, I see nothing," she smiles at him.

"Whenever you're ready, we're ready," he says also smiling.

"We are going to Mama on the Grand Concourse?" she asks.

He frowns, a little irritated at her. "Esther, I work tomorrow. We'll go Saturday morning when the train is empty."

Esther watches her brother open the dresser drawer and take out a pair of blue socks. He's so easy with her; it's as if they've been together a whole lifetime and he hadn't left Warsaw when she was twelve years old.

"I want to tell you something," he says peering down at his blue socks as if admiring them.

"So?"

"Mama's not what you remember."

"I remember so many different things," Esther answers, looking at his bowed head.

"No, I mean *oyverbotl* – senile, not right in the head. She repeats the same things over and over. She forgets. She accuses. She can't remember who's who sometimes," he says. Then he pulls off his left sock and throws it in the wastebasket.

"Why do that, Hershel?"

"It has a hole in it," he answers and takes off the other sock too.

"I don't like it when my wife goes to the country."

On Saturday morning the three of them take the elevated train at 177th Street to the Grand Concourse station. Esther dresses herself very carefully in a red-flowered blouse and light tan skirt. When she looks in the mirror she can see her own strong resemblance to Mama: the hooked nose, the blue eyes, the teeth spaced widely apart. A disquieting, disjointed thought occurs to her: I am the same age now as Mama was when she left me to go to The Bronx. But how can she forgive me for marrying Itzik and not coming to America if she doesn't recognize me?

When they ascend the stairs to the IRT 177th Street Station after one o'clock, deep rain clouds are piled darkly in the distance. Esther hears resounding thunder as she enters the train Herschel calls "the local." At first the train moves along high above the crowded tenement streets. Esther can even see into the windows of the people who live so close to the train; she feels she could almost touch them. But after a while the train enters a dark tunnel, clattering, jerking her back and forth until it stops at a sign: *The Grand Concourse.* Herschel takes her by the hand and leads her and Itzik out of the train, along the concrete platform, up two steep flights of stairs, and into the bright sunlight. The street is much wider than the one on which Herschel lives and the buildings are higher, more luxurious, and more elegant.

Nothing like that even in Haifa. So much red brick.

"That's the one," Hershel says turning to Esther and pointing to a six-story building across the street. "That's Mama's building. Zelde and her two boys live on the third floor, front, 3B. Mama has a little room that faces the street."

As they go up the tiny elevator with a marble floor and glass walls, Esther's heart is beating so fast, so irregularly, and so strong, she has to take a long breath. She moves in front of Hershel and Itzik and knocks on the door of apartment 3B. Immediately a young boy with curly black hair opens it.

"Aunt Esther," he declares, quickly stepping aside to leave her exposed to everyone in the apartment.

Everyone seated at the table stares at her; each seems to strain for some faint recognition. Esther would like to disappear on the spot. A very thin woman dressed in a sleeveless summer pinafore rises from the table, walks right up to her and grabs her around the shoulders, holding her close. Her perfume is strong lilac.

"My sister," she shouts into Esther's ear, but Esther isn't sure which sister this is, and so she just leaves her arms hanging at her side.

Now everyone is getting up and hugging her and hugging Itzik. No one introduces themselves, so Esther is not sure who is who, and she can't focus her feelings directly. Love, wonder, shyness, longing, even revulsion course through her body, as if she had just finished off a whole bottle of vodka in one gulp.

Esther's first words are, "Where's Mama?"

"It's her nap time," the thin sister whispers. "But go in, go in, wake her up. But wait, she may not know you, even though she often says, 'Esther'l, my Esther'l, when is she coming?' Just say your name very slowly. She may know 'Esther,' even though she doesn't remember our names most of the time.

"Mama is waiting for me from then, as I was when I was a girl," Esther thinks desperately, "Oh, how I failed her."

The young boy who called her "Aunt" takes Esther by her cold hand and leads her down a dark corridor to a screened door. Then he leaves her and runs away. Peering in through the screen, she sees a very old woman seated looking out over a wide open porch window. She is wearing a brown *shaytl* – the same exact one she wore in Warsaw – and a long gray dress and black-laced shoes. The same dress, the same shoes.

"It's me, Mama," Esther says softly as she opens the door.

"It's going to rain, Esther'l," Feyge says, not turning to look at her daughter.

"You know me, Mama?" Esther asks, frozen to the spot, both her feet nailed to the ground.

"I shouldn't know you? I sent you tickets. I'm satisfied you're here, but such a bad day to come like this in the rain."

The old woman turns around in her chair. Her eyes are deep blue, sharp and clear.

"I want you first to move in with Zelde for a few months, look around, and then you can get a job."

"A job?"

"Can you sew?"

"Mama, I'm married. I have seven beautiful children, almost grown up."

Feyge laughs derisively. "Seven children are too many children. You shouldn't have so many children. In America no one has so many children," she chides her daughter.

100

"I came from *Eretz Yisroel*," Esther answers, as she pulls up a green wobbly porch chair and sits next to her mother.

"Go away," Feyge says. "I tell you not to go there. There is too much fighting. I have a daughter in *Eretz Yisroel*. She married a fool. I told her he was no good, but she didn't listen to me."

"Mama, it is me, Esther. I married Itzik. I went to *Yisroel*. I'm here to visit you." Esther touches her mother's arm. The arm is so frail, so boney. A flood of deepest love and sorrow sweeps over her. Esther folds her hands together, moving her body back and forth. Crying. Her chair creaks rhythmically.

"You know," Feyge replies, "I always love a rainy day. When it rains in The Bronx, I always tell my children it rains everywhere in the world. Even in *Eretz Yisroel*.

"I'm sorry, Mama," Esther repeats. Suddenly, she feels a terrible anger welling up in her, decades of anger, sticking in her throat, but she slowly swallows, breathing deeply. "It doesn't rain the same time in *Yisroel* as it does in The Bronx, Mama. You should know that by now."

Feyge has closed her eyes and fallen asleep.

The rain begins to fall at first in small drops and then within minutes there is a torrential downpour. Esther holds her mother close to her, breathing with her, delighting in the embrace and the sounds of the rain on the street below.

GOD MOTHER
Candice Rowe

The neighbors find you on the couch,
a tiny gray child with one sock on
and one sock off,
a carton of milk in the toaster oven...
a fall from your past culinary virtuosity,
I might add.
I bring you take-out pizza,
and you nibble away,
squirreling me a look,
afraid I might take it back before
you've licked the past from your bony fingers.

God Mother, I say to the room empty
even with you in it.
The ceiling yellowed from that dead man's cigars.
The blue and white ceramic horses holding
their warped candles, yellow too;
one of them looking at me askance.

Everything is the same.
Thanksgiving is a hard rosewood chair
with brocaded cushion,
the same old
Sit Up Straight
Don't Eat With your Fingers.
Christmas the old,
I'll Spank You For Your Own Good
If You Don't Eat Every Lick On Your Plate.
Marshmallows looming like ottomans,
a single string bean the Nile.

I like you like this. I can leave my crust.
I can make foot marks in the pile of your rug.
I can run my tongue over my teeth inside my mouth,
bulging out the lips.
And still you smile at me.
The only trace of God Mother is in your hands.
Busy with their smoothing and knit picking,
busy with holding the world together,
one lamb chop at a time.

DANCING IN THE WIND
Sallie Tisdale

Maud is eighty-six years old and weighs just that many pounds. She is nearly bald; her thin, fine white-gray hair has been rubbed nearly away by all her years in bed. Maud had a stroke years ago, and then another and another. She doesn't open her eyes, never speaks. She is fed with a big plastic syringe that the nurses slip past her resisting lips; the right amount of pureed chicken or spinach tickles the back of the tongue and makes her swallow, involuntarily.

Tonight I discover Maud has cellulitus, an odd but common infection under the skin. Her right hip and buttock are red, swollen, and hot; she has a temperature of 104. I call her doctor. He asks me, "If you were her granddaughter, would you want me to treat her?" "I'm not her granddaughter," I answer. "You know," he sighs, alone in his office, wanting to go home, "I promised that lady years ago that I wouldn't keep her alive like this." He pauses, and I wait. "I promised her." Eventually he orders an antibiotic, because of the slight chance Maud's infection could spread to another patient, and her temperature drops in the evening, and she goes on.

I am often asked how I can stand my work, and I know that it is this very going on that my questioners mean. Not only the uninitiated, but other nurses and physicians often dislike this "gutter work" that I do: part-time charge nurse in an old, not very good, urban nursing home, working with the sickest patients, the ones who won't recover from an unfortunate age. Some of the nurses I work with are always looking for a "better" job, competing with thousands of other nurses for the hospital positions grown suddenly scarce in recent years – hospital jobs where patients come and go, quickly, and sometimes get well.

I feel a measure of peace here, a sense of belonging that is rare for me anywhere else. Partly it is because I know what to do, because I am competent here. Over the years, though, the ease that I've felt since my first job as a nurse's aide when I was eighteen has become layered with fondness, the way one grows used to a house and its little quirks, the slightly warped kitchen floor, the sighing upstairs window. Here all is aslant, and I have to tilt my head a bit to see it clearly.

Coming in to begin a shift, I pass the activity room, crowded with hump-backed white-haired people asleep in their wheelchairs, facing a man playing *The Star Spangled Banner* on a musical saw. In the corner, one upright, perfectly bald man spins slowly round and round in his chair, like a wind-up doll, bumping the wall at last and spinning back the other way. This is a scene of astonishing absurdity, and no one is paying any attention to it. We take it for granted, like the faint, lingering smell of urine tinged with kitchen steam and disinfectant.

I leave the elevator on the third floor and step into the furnace heat of July without air-conditioning and the queer conversation of the confused that will dog my steps all evening long. They give me this gift of skewed perspective like a gift of non-Euclidean sight, so that I become as willing to dip and bend with the motion of a damaged cortex as a tree in wind. I pass medicine room to room, and in each room the televisions are tuned to the same channel. For my 4:00 pass, it is *People's Court*, plaintiff and defendant, as I travel down the hall. At 6:00 we watch *Jeopardy*. "What is the only military medal that can be given to non-combatants?" asks the host on the T.V. in Monte's room; then we pass next door to Sylvia, and together we guess: "The Medal of Honor." And we are right. Bent over a task, preoccupied, I am startled by the peculiar speech of the nerve-worn, its sudden clarity. Up here, each day is the same, a refrain, and nothing can be taken for granted, nothing.

I know how many people hate nursing homes – hate the word, the notion, the possibility. A friend of mine lives next door to a local nursing home, and she tells me she hears people screaming in the evening, unseen, their voices leaping the tall fence between her house and the home. She assumes the worst, my friend: that they scream from neglect, from abuse, from terror. She says it is a "terrible place," never having been inside.

105

I tell her that in every nursing home there are people who scream; they scream without warning at private phantoms. I ask her where such people should go. I ask her how she would stop them from screaming. She listens, and I know she is unconvinced. "Nursing homes are terrible places," she says, and it is because what happens there is terrible.

(I am similarly fearful around big machinery, in boiler rooms and factories. I am out of place, adrift, and fear the worst; is that shower of sparks routine, or does it signal disaster? What is that loud noise?)

I enjoy my work, but I enjoy it in moments that are separated from each other by long stretches of fatigue and concentration. I enjoy it best when it's over. I catch myself, hot and worn at the end of the day, hoping the man I keep expecting to die will live until the next shift. I get irritable. The clock creeps past 11:30, past midnight, and I'm still sitting with my feet propped up, trying to decipher my scribbled notes. The undone tasks, the unexplained events that want explaining, badger and chafe. And everybody dies.

My ideals twitch on occasion, like a dog's leg in a dream. I want no one to lie in urine for a moment; I want every ice pitcher always filled. For a long while, for many years, I disliked the use of sedatives and anti-psychotics to knock out the wound-up chatter and restless, disoriented souls. The orders read: "PRN agitation" – as necessary – and this is the nurse's power to ignore, and the power to mute. So easy to misuse, so simple. But as a shot of morphine can break the spiraling cycle of pain, so can a spiral of panic be broken – not for my comfort, but for the comfort of the panicked.

Sadie screams at me from far down the hall: "Help! It's an emergency!" And she screams over and over, rocking back and forth, till I come to see; she leans over and points at the blazing fire she sees and hears and smells, raging out of control. I see no fire. I coo to her, hushing; she babbles on. Finally I lie beside her on the bed; she is stiff and yearns to leap up. And, at last, I go to prepare the syringe. "From the doctor," I tell her, because Sadie loves her medicine, and she falls asleep.

The responsibility is mine; the consequences are mine. I have to be sure about choices no one can be sure about. I call for nurse's aides to come and hold the flailing arms and legs of Charlie, more than six feet tall, furious at the world that confounds him so. He squirms and tries to bite me when I hit his hip with the needle. We fall across the bed together, grunting. And I know that the visitor, passing by, sees only the force, the convenience, the terrible thing we have done to this person: the abduction.

The same is true of the smell, just barely there, acrid in the heat. It's true of the drooling, the patter of nonsense in the dining room. Visitors tremble, knowing Grandma is here, and wish they had the courage to bring her home, out of this awful place.

Could this inadvertent audience, my patients' families, see these scenes and believe me when I say it is a labor of love? Some do; they bake blueberry pastries and doughnuts for the nurses, pat us on the arm, cluck their tongues. "I don't know how you stand it," the niece says, after an afternoon at Aunt Louise's bedside.

The difference here is in what we call love, the gap of definition between their words and mine. Their burden – and they seem to really want to know – is a burden of despair, a personal burden, bred of fear and impotence in equal amounts. This personal despair imagines as its opposite, its anima, a personal love and a personal sorrow. The visitor sees May defecating helplessly on the rug before anyone can stop her, and it strikes his identity, his self. It is as though the observer himself stood there, revealed. I have the advantage of knowing May will forget it in an hour; he does not. In breathless confession, waiting for the elevator, the visitor says: "I pray to God I die before this happens to me." I am told this again and again. "I pray to God." A kind of ego-terror is born, and with unbordered empathy comes flight. Suddenly the sounds and smells oppress, overwhelm. Suddenly it's time, more than time, to go.

A labor of love, love for fading people who dwell in shadows. I am saved from the need for flight – I am uninjured – because I let them do their own suffering. This is a cold-sounding excuse, I know. Call it compassion instead of love. (I am surprised and pleased, just now, to find that Roget's Thesaurus lists as a synonym for compassion and kindness the less lofty "disinterested-

107

ness.") I have learned not to make personal what I see; not, as it were, to anthropomorphize my patients' experience.

Just as the witness imagines himself complete, transformed to this place and trapped, so does he grant full imagination to those who are. He assumes Maud is aware of her plight, ruminates on her fate. I grant Maud plenty, without granting full cognizance in her withered brain. Down the hall from Maud is a man in his forties who is paralyzed from polio and limited to a respirator. He is fully cognizant – no pity for him either. Pity makes distance, creates a separation of witness and participant; by assuming a person is absorbed in suffering, the witness prohibits them from participation in anything else.

I close the curtains and keep my voice down, as a point of etiquette as much as sympathy. I have a spring in my step; I can see and hear; I can eat and digest and control my urine, and I know these for the blessings they are. I am young enough still, to take care of the old. But these are the most transient of graces, these graces of health, and I might lose them all tomorrow if the brakes fail. Old and sick comes later – but it comes.

Here everybody dies. We tell black jokes. I laugh and laugh at a cartoon of an old man sitting up in bed, surrounded by impatient doctors: "These are my last words," the old man says. "No, these are my last words. No, no, wait..." We have a three-part mythos of death here, and first is that no one dies when we think they will, always later. Second, if a person long ill and silent suddenly comes to life, he or she will die soon. And last, people die in threes. Within a day or week of one death will follow two more. Just last week, Monte died, days after we'd predicted, and now Mr. H. down the hall is talking again, after months of sleep.

Death is anticipated, waited on in suspense. It is like waiting in a very long line that snakes around a corner so you can't see the end. When the last breath is drawn it is startling; here is a breath, and another, and another. Death is the breath after the last one. Always fresh, always solemn, and not unlike a childbirth; the living let their own held breaths go, and smile, and in the solemnity is an affirmation. Here it is. I stroke the skin so suddenly and mysteriously waxen. I pull out tubes and patch holes. I like dead bodies; at no other time am I so aware of my own

108

animation. It isn't because I am lucky and this poor fool is not, but because here before me is the mute, incontrovertible evidence. Some force drives these shells, and it drives me still. I am a witness, an attestant, to a forsworn truth.

Still I have my own despair. For me it is the things undone that break my back sometimes, the harried rush with people calling, and all those unexplained events. I wish we could ferret out the meaning in all this chaos, talk it out. No time – sometimes the ice pitchers are dry all night. Last week I had a shift like this, split in the middle by an impatient doctor who snapped his fingers at me and tapped his toe in frustration at my slowness. An hour later another doctor dropped by, and I asked her to see a new patient with a minor but uncomfortable problem. She refused, and then explained: "Medicine is the kind of job where you have to be really careful not to let people take advantage of you," she said. "Somebody always wants something." And all I could do was look at her and get back to work.

In my first job as an aide, I cared for a Swedish woman named Florence, who had only one leg. She was happy and confused, and didn't know she'd lost her limb. Time and again she would try to walk, and fall. I tied her in her chair, in her bed, and over and over she managed to untie herself and fall, thud, to the hard tile floor. She was always surprised. Exasperated at last, I stood over her and asked, "What am I going to do with you?" And she looked up from where she sprawled and said, "Don't stop trying, dear."

Don't stop trying. This is far from the best nursing home, but it isn't the worst. I rant and jump to complain, go home frustrated. It should be better. But the sheets are changed, people are fed, for the most part each one is treated with kindness – a clumsy, patronizing kindness at times, but many of them don't discriminate these fine points. Kindness is enough.

I like dead people and all their apprenticed fellows like Maud, who, slowly, is learning to die. And I like this place, with its cockeyed, terpsichorean logic. I will feed Maud her squirts of puree, and a few minutes later Sadie will announce she is the Queen of Germany and requires royal treatment. Celia will cough up blood, and, as I consider my options, I will hear distant bed rails shake, the curses, the rhythmic, pattering singsong.

Sometimes the borders shift even further. I sprawl across a bed, fiddling with Roberta's leaking catheter, trying to disentangle her fingers from my hair. The tube feeding drips on my leg. Who is keeper, who is kept? This is the Marx Brothers all grown up, slapstick matured, life imitating art imitating life. Down the hall the Greek chorus begins, explaining the meaning and the mystery as the melodramatic story limps along.

CLOSE CALLS
Pamela C. Ullman

Out of nowhere, she cuts me off, pigtails waving in the breeze, the sleeves of a fuzzy old sweater looped tightly around her neck. In her wake, all the world turns pink, like a cherry tree that's blossomed overnight. I cozy up to the curb and wait. When she zips around again, she nearly whacks my side-view mirror with her handlebar. Astonished and maybe just a little bit afraid, I slink way down in my seat, ever watchful over the dash, until she rides off into the sunset.

As soon as I get home, I call my father.

"She's happy," I tell him, pleased to be able to report the truth.

"How could you tell?"

"Because she was fast, Dad. Pink and lovely and sure. She turned the leaves on the trees inside out."

"A beautiful woman," he says.

The next day, she's got company – a pony-tailed man on a mountain bike in hot pursuit of a pink comet. His front tire flirts aggressively with the firm rear end of her Schwinn Classic, tailgating way too close for my comfort. I roll down the window of my gas-guzzling SUV, and consider elbowing him off his saddle on the next pass. They whiz on by, but I'm paralyzed. The pink lady's laughter lags behind like my best perfume. This time, I reach for my cell phone.

"I think Mom's got a boyfriend," I tell my father.

"Well, good for her," he says, miles away from meaning it. "Older or younger?"

"Somewhere between Kirk Douglas and Gregory Peck."

"Not as good lookin' as either, I hope."

"Looks a little like Rip Van Winkle."

"Hell, Maggie! That's no competition!" The emphysema turns his chuckle to a gag; I hear him reach for the oxygen. When he catches his breath and I'm sure he's OK, we hang up.

On my next visit, the streets around the hospital are quiet and barren of bicycles. I race up the walkway and punch the doorbell with my fist. A new breed of doctor in khakis and sandals ushers me in. The absence of white has a calming effect on my nerves.

"Looking for Daisy Thoms," I say without ado or explanation.

"It's arts and crafts time," he beams. "Perhaps you'd like to visit."

In the Rec Room, the patients are limbering up the right sides of their brains with finger paint, construction paper, and Play-Doh – all the sights and sounds of nursery school. Weaponless arts for the semi-dangerous. The sharpest tool in the room is a pair of rounded scissors, the kind that can barely cut paper, much less skin.

My mother stands alone, in a corner by the window. Between the line of a surgical mask and the sweet bunch of a plastic shower cap, I find her eyes, forever green and hopeful. When I take her in my arms, a newspaper rustles beneath our feet like leaves. Mom shakes her cans of spray paint like a pair of maracas and wiggles her still narrow hips in red and white-checked peddle pushers. She looks good and I tell her so. She holds out a can and asks if I feel like helping. I shake it a few times, hard enough to hear the ping of the color ball as it bounces around inside. We tape the "Metro" section of the newspaper across the tires and wrap "Weddings and Engagements" around the handlebars. Mom stripes every few inches of pink paint with masking tape until the bike looks like a candy cane past its prime. When we are through, she takes my arm and pulls me over to the window seat where we sit and admire our handiwork.

"Now that's a sight to behold," I say, both proud and afraid. One minute she is under my skin. The next she is gone. I have to remind myself to breathe.

"I'm racing in the Tour de France," she confides with a wink, the kind she used to give me when she needed my help to pull one over on Dad. "Be my co-conspirator!" she would beg, laughing, irresistibly everything. I take her hand in my lap, stroke the thread of calluses that meanders down the side of her palm, just next to the lumps and bumps she got from playing tennis and planting tulip bulbs. "How'd you get these?" I ask, still fingering the line

112

of dots beneath her pinky. "From shifting my multi-speed Rocket 88 around the hills of Provence," she says with another wink. She turns toward the window, fixes on a squirrel in a tree. I kiss her cheek and tell her I'll be back tomorrow. She smells like spring.

When I get home, the phone is ringing.

"She thinks she's competing in the Tour de France," I tell Dad. "She's spray-painted her bike all red and white and blue." His breathing is loud and raspy, like rain on sandpaper. It stops my heart for a second, inviting me to confess that I helped with the paint.

"Paris here we come!" he says.

It's scary how much he loves her.

In the basement, I haul out a box of photos and scrapbooks, curled and crinkled from the damp. It takes a while to find what I think I remember – a black and white snapshot of my mother on a tricycle, both done up with streamers for the Fourth of July. Upstairs in my room, I close the door and stand before the mirror. I hold her image alongside my own, and I wonder what this life may have in store for me.

DETAILS
Thomas Michael McDade

The hitchhiker didn't say much, and conversation was the reason I'd stopped for him; the radio didn't work and I was lonely as hell. I was driving from Providence to Denver in a '55 Ford for which I'd paid seventy-five dollars. Just before he fell asleep, he wound up his description of his job with some advice. "Don't ever work in a fertilizer factory if you can help it," he said, and I've yet to work in one.

So now I'm driving again, but not to Denver. Just a little local trip and I find myself looking into the clear blue sky where I see the hitchhiker step away from the old Ford, onto the Iowa highway. It's a good thing the daydream ended when it did, or I would have run into the car ahead of me. So far I've had to slam on the brakes three times. I resolve to keep my eyes off the sky. I resolve to stop running away from the present to the trivial details of my past.

My car is new and the radio works very well. I turn on the ballgame. I follow the ball from the pitcher's hand to the catcher's glove, stopping at every stitch. The announcer says that the fastball is really hopping; the batters are looking at a pill. That's a coincidence, pills are involved in today's mission, but I can't think about them now. I take my mind off the stitches and all of the major league autographs of my boyhood fill the ball until it is black. Jim Rice hits into a double play. I picture my father shaking his head and saying, "I told you so." The station identifies itself.

I study the license plate in front of me. Like a child playing a traveling game on a long vacation drive, I add numbers and attach words to letters. I wonder whether it was a murderer who made the plate? Maybe I'm looking at tomorrow's number. I count the rust spots on the bumper.

I read somewhere that murderers are sometimes obsessed with trivial details. Their minds fly from thoughts that might bring remorse. They also play children's games, connecting the molecules of sidewalks, walls, floors, and people like dots in a coloring book. They don't stare at any spot too long. An upsetting image might form, like when you focus on a cloud too long. There might be a gun, a knife, or a corpse. At times, they slam their eyes shut to study the flashing colors or they count the stars. Going to sleep, they hope for fleeting dreams with details like soothing fingers, but those digits may turn to fishhooks and ruin their peace. Yet the hooks can be spread on the sky, placed back to back to resemble faraway birds. Temporarily calm, the killers search for more dots, and those dots could be pills.

I am no murderer, but I have made my first connection with death. In my pocket there's a deed to my father's gravesite in the Veteran's cemetery. He's finally a landowner. Attached to the deed is a reservation for my mother, just like going to a fine restaurant or taking an exotic vacation. I haven't been to the cemetery since the hearse dropped him off; nor have I visited my mother since she went to the nursing home.

Today I will visit, and I wonder how many tears I have left for her. Maybe none will be needed. I have a bottle of pills in my pocket that were advertised in the back of a health magazine. The ad said they could restore memory, and I called in an order immediately. I wonder how many other sons sent in their money? I switch stations, looking for classical music that will move me to some distant shore where I can look out and count the waves. I find none and settle for a Million-Dollar Weekend. The Beatles sing about being sixty-four. Nine years ago she was sixty-four. The car in front of me turns left, and I have a new plate to study. Out of the corner of my eye I see the Texaco station. If I can find another detail to hide in, I might miss the street and get a reprieve.

Instead I turn the corner and see a housing project to my left. The blocks are different from the ones I'm used to: there are wooden buildings among the brick. You might mistake them for normal apartments. The nursing home is across from them. It's made of the same kind of brick as the project where I grew up, and not that shiny stuff that tries to pass for brick in the newfangled housing projects.

She got away from the project for seventeen years, only to be surrounded by brick in the end, like an ember in a kiln.

No, they don't make housing projects the way they used to. Maybe they don't make sons the way they used to either. I tune in the ballgame again. Perhaps the pills have lost their potency; three home runs have been hit. I park in the space reserved for doctors.

A lump is coming to my throat. I remember a movie where Michael Caine beat a brainwashing attempt by digging a nail into his palm. My details are as ineffective as the fastball and a nail wouldn't work either. I wish I had felt all of this sympathy for her when I was young and screwing up.

In the lobby there is a book to sign. I'm logging in as Petty Officer of the watch on some sad gray destroyer. Perhaps I should look at the brighter side. I'm visiting an art gallery. The nurse behind the plexiglas hits the buzzer and I'm admitted. A prison door slamming behind me would afford more comfort. Ahead of me is the chapel. Through the opened door I see stained glass comforting the sunlight. The glass is like the stained glass above the Stations of the Cross in my childhood church, and I remember my soul mingling with all those colors, occasionally returning for the music. Color and music, color and music.

The elevator opens and I step into a cell. I close my eyes and imagine a prisoner doing reverent push-ups in front of a pinup, as he dreams of schemes designed to sabotage license plates with obscenities. Opening my eyes, I read the emergency instructions on the wall. The elevator jerks to a halt and I experience a touch of roller coaster. Maybe that is what death is like. Two flies leave with me when the door opens.

An old man, dapper with his bowtie, explains to a nurse that he had no intention of leaving. He just happened to be passing the elevator. When she turns and walks away from him, he wrinkles up his face like a twisted rubber band and launches a glob of spit at her. It lands on his shoe. No one is at the desk. I look down the hall and see a woman who probably weighs sixty pounds sitting in a wheelchair eating lunch. The plate looks like it holds twenty pounds of food. She takes a piece of meat in her fingers and picks from the gristle. Near her are two finches in a cage.

116

A tough-looking nurse arrives at the desk. When she last combed her hair, she might have had teasing on her mind, but didn't follow through. For a second, she holds her cigarette between her teeth, pulls back her lips, and directs me to my mother's room. On the way down the hall, I'm approached by a woman who asks me for a cigarette. She is as skinny as the one in the wheelchair and her face is a withered milkweed pod. When I offer her a dollar to buy some, she takes it suspiciously. I don't know how much cigarettes cost; perhaps I should have given her more.

My mother is awake. Her mattress is jacked up and she stares at the closet. I kiss her and smile. Sitting on the bedside chair, my eyes fill with tears. She says nothing when I ask how she is feeling. She goes back to staring at the closet, and there is no response when I ask her if she knows who I am. When she holds up her hand to study it, the tiny wedding ring drops to the base of her finger. She doesn't know she's a widow. The hand goes down on the blanket. I wonder whether she will take the pills.

Once I took a philosophy course in night school called "Existentialism," where the professor talked about man as a "bag of guts with eyes." I argued then, but I wouldn't be so dogmatic now. They say this disease erases the mind backwards. Maybe she is experiencing her girlhood again and I don't exist. Or, could it all be an act? She might have gotten tired of her life and bolted into another one, just like the man with the bowtie who wants to bolt this place. "Hey mom, give me a cameo part in one of your reruns, just another kid on the block. Wave to me. Blink your eyes twice if you can't wave."

I start making promises to God. "I'll worship you if you bring her back, just for a second." I feel like the little boy who put his toy drum before a statue of the baby Jesus and demanded that he play. She doesn't blink, and Jesus wasn't Ringo. She stares straight into my eyes. Her eyes are filmy, tired. She looks pregnant. She probably gets the same twenty-pound ration as the bird lady.

I take her hand and hope that there is some link that is stronger than this foolish disease. I try to force my love across the link. I think I know what love is now that Dad's gone. I never got around to saying it, but I always wrote it on letters and cards, didn't I? Maybe I only said it when I was drunk.

117

I missed the big deathbed scene with Dad. I know I would have told him then. Even though I didn't know what it was, I would have told him. So goddamned precise, I measured my words and feelings with a micrometer to be sure they matched. I was temperate about all the wrong things. "I love you, Ma. You don't know what I'm talking about, and I am punished. Never mind the word; I acted it sometimes, didn't I? The silence, it's the silence I can't stand. You're like that goddamned hitchhiker. I wish I had taped your voice. Then maybe death and your disease wouldn't be so bad. Please, let something move, anything. Let my apologies go to you, send back forgiveness." She breaks wind. No embarrassment, only a baby's look of bewilderment.

A woman comes in the door. She is some kind of religious layperson and she wants to know if my mother wants communion. I tell her my mom doesn't know what communion is. In the back of my mind, a little nun lectures on the possibility of a miraculous recovery through communion, and I almost call the lady back. Then I realize I have the miracle, the communion in my pocket. But can she take the pills? All of her food has to be pureed.

"I see you saying your tattered novenas, reading Father Payton's rosary book with death's prayer cards for bookmarks. I see you walking in the rain to church, counting on your rosary in your pocket. You are upset because you forgot the budget envelope. How many times did I send you to your knees? Remember all those raffle tickets for the Columban Fathers' cars? You never won. The consolation prize is a closet to stare at and a maudlin son."

I'm getting timid about the miracle pills. They're probably a hoax anyway. What if she should choke on them? Maybe it would be best. God's will, so to speak. I haven't looked at my watch yet. I feel like a runner who's promised himself not to look at his watch until he has reached a certain mile marker. How much time is enough? How much do I owe? Does it make any difference whether I come or not? "You have a worried look on your face. It's the one I remember most. Please smile. When I leave here I want to be able to think of you with a smile." She looks like she might be trying to say something, but yawns instead. "If you could only talk, it's the voice that's the soul, isn't it?"

118

I've got to do it. There's a pitcher of water with a glass straw on the bed stand. I pour some and take the pills out of my pocket. They're as big as M&M peanuts. It says "take one a day" on the label, but I'll give her three: three for the Trinity. I slip one into her mouth and offer the straw. She drinks and I give her another one. She handles it well. She starts to choke on the third one and I panic. What will I tell the nurses? I roll her on her side and slap her back. There is no more coughing and she is still. I look at her face and she is smiling. I smile back and the smile disappears. She starts shouting, "Bastard, bastard, bastard..." Never in her life did she talk like that. The nurse comes in and tells me I had better leave.

I want to run, but instead I walk slowly, studying the highly polished gray tile beneath my feet. The lady who asked me for a cigarette must have had enough money; she breezes past me on the right smoking up a storm. She stops quickly and turns around. "Bastard," she says. The bird lady nods in her sleep. The dapper man leans forward in his chair like a sprinter at the starting line. The nurse at the desk gives me a dirty look.

The flies are back in the elevator. I sign out quickly and run to my car. The game is still on. The announcer is telling an anecdote about Yogi Berra meeting Hemingway. Maybe if I crush up the rest of the pills and sprinkle them on my father's grave he will talk. Jesus, it was like she was making up for all the cursing she never did.

After driving for a few minutes, I see a guy hitchhiking. Thinking that company might be just the thing, I stop. He starts talking nonstop about baseball. I'm happy to talk with him. Then he gets into trivia.

"I'm going to pay you for this ride by letting you in on one of the best trivia questions I've ever heard," he says.

"Have you ever worked in a fertilizer factory?" I ask.

"What the hell's that got to do with baseball?" he says, looking at me like I'm crazy.

"Nothing, nothing, you just remind me of a guy I used to know who worked in a fertilizer factory."

"Wait a minute, man; you're not insulting me, are you?"

"Hell no, get on with the question," I reply.

"Name five pitchers who won the Cy Young award and at one time or another played for the Mets," he asks.

"Tom Seaver."

"That's the easy one," he says.

"Shit, I'm a Red Sox fan, what do you know about the Mets?"

"Want the answer?"

"Give me a couple of minutes," I say, as I reach into my pocket and take out the pill bottle. I empty it into my hand, almost hitting the car in front of me. I pop them like candy.

"What the hell are you doing, man? Watch the road."

"Spahn, Warren Spahn," I say. "These pills are going to find those players for me. Dean Chance."

"Let me out of here, you're crazy."

"I'll take you to Iowa."

"Stop, goddamit," he shouts.

I pull over and he jumps out.

"How about Mike Marshall...Randy Jones? Come back you bastard; I have all the answers.

Bastard, no good bastard!"

HIS UNJUST DESSERT
Bara Swain

Armed with strawberries, Cool Whip and Norton's critical edition of *Madame Bovary*, I pranced down three ominous corridors, past two nursing stations and beyond a vending machine that caused pleasure or displeasure when it dispensed incorrect change. Negotiating the last locked door to my final destination, I charged down the hallway, bobbing my head in recognition to a nurse here, an aide there, until my sister's red tank top signaled my successful, albeit late, arrival. She sat regally, like a cardinal amongst a flock of pigeons, in the enclosed arboretum that boasted one slender tree and one sturdy table of wrought iron whose strength and endurance juxtaposed the fragile man beside it, framed by a stainless steel wheelchair and, on occasion, my sister's random embrace.

The man was my father. He removed his cap, shouted obscenities at Hitler, urged my sister to boycott California grapes, called to his dead mother and John Wayne, recited the first verse of Ferlinghetti's Underwear, and returned the cap to his head. It was one of those headgears of composite order in which we can find the threads of his former self, woven between the faded McGovern/Shriver logo and unpolished buttons that reflected only the most intense light: MAKE LOVE NOT WAR, Save a Tree, COME HOME AMERICA, Pro-Choice, STRIKE, I Love My Grandpa, I HAD A DREAM.

Wordlessly, I knelt beside my father, lay my head in his lap, and nuzzled the chicken chow mein stain on his faded Chinos. He stroked my hair in silence. I raised my face to gaze into his steel blue eyes. He tipped the peak of his cap with an unsure hand. "You look just like my favorite daughter," he said. My sister scowled and counted loose change. I counted his coffee-stained teeth.

"Dad," I whispered, "I *am* your favorite daughter." My father looked at me with the depths of expression on an imbecile's face. One bold tear rolled off the tip of his Jewish nose, as he turned his gaze to the young sapling. His jaw dropped open and I shoveled the white-capped strawberries into his mouth, one spoon after another, causing neither pleasure nor displeasure, filling the formidable silence with elaborate descriptions of Kraft's use of non-dairy products and Flaubert's use of metaphor, until his unjust dessert, laced in literary uncertainty, was another fleeting memory. Fate willed it this way.

THE BLUE DRESS
Siv Cedering

I will go to my mother's house.
A white-haired woman will come to the door.
She will hesitate, wait until a light
Will light her face.
Am I her sister? Her mother? Her daughter?
She will know I have been there before.
"Daughter, is it you? Come in.
Close the door. Close the door."

The doors in my mother's mind
Are closing, one by one.
She cannot remember my name.
She cannot remember the name of her son.
She cannot remember the color of his eyes.
My blue-eyed brother has been lost for years.
How will he ever be found, if his mother
Does not remember the color of his eyes,
If she does not remember his name,
Or mine?

How do I go to my mother's house
When even the light that occasionally lights
That last room
Is losing its shine?
Somewhere way back,
There was a new dress that was blue.
She remembers that dress. She wants one.
I buy her a new blue dress. What else
Can I do? A light flickers
In her eyes.
There is something about the color blue.

How do I go there,
And what will I do,
When all the rooms have closed, one by one,
And the blue dress is gone
With the color of my brother's eyes,
His name, and mine?
How do I go to my mother's house
To close her eyes
For that last time?

MAGGIE
Ann G. Thomas

As she walked, she had been looking to her left at tall rocks whose ancient crevices mirrored her own. To her right the ocean crashed, blue becoming white, becoming the mustard color of churning sand in foam. Earlier she had passed a retriever and a man. The man's footprints paralleled the dog's clover-shaped indentations in the wet sand, left just far enough back to escape the ocean's sweep. Then – escaping until found by her foot – there was the large pile left by the dog. Maggie stood looking downward. Excrement oozed from beneath the sole of her wet, sand-encrusted shoe. She rubbed the shoe back and forth on a strip of seaweed before retreating to a shelter provided by a turn in the rock wall. A piece of driftwood served as a chair where she sat, an audience of one, for the symphony of crashing surf and screaming gulls. At some point she looked down at the watch.

"Soon."

Although the watch was hers now, she still thought of it as Suzanne's – a present she had given her forty-two years ago when they first moved in together. Suzanne had worn it daily until four years ago when she took it off and put it on Maggie's wrist.

"Why Suz?" Maggie asked.

Suzanne hadn't answered. Maggie imagined Suzanne knew time had stopped for her.

"Are you sure?" Maggie had asked first one doctor and then many, but the answer was always the same. Even without the doctors, there was no mistaking the slow removal of Suzanne's connection to the world the two shared.

Forgetfulness was the beginning, nothing earth-shattering, just simple forgetfulness. Maggie would find ice cream in the refrigerator, melted into drink-like consistency. Suzanne would be unable to find her billfold

125

or remember why she had gone into a room. But those were ordinary kinds of forgetting. They joked about having "senior-moments." Suzanne made lists and became compulsive about putting everything where it belonged. For a while it seemed that things improved. Neither talked about what was happening. Suzanne was ashamed and Maggie was frightened.

One October afternoon, Suzanne went to the grocery store. Maggie was busy, only half registering the "be gone only a few minutes" that Suz had shouted as she left. Later she looked up and realized it was dark and Suzanne had been gone a long time. She looked at the clock. It was almost nine.

Looking out the window at the empty driveway, she could feel her stomach tighten. Visions of crushed fenders and worse flashed in her mind as she tried to formulate a plan.

She was reaching for the phone when she saw the lights of a car. Running outside, she stopped at the sight of a policeman helping Suzanne out of a patrol car.

"You know her ma'am?" the policeman asked. "She was wandering the Safeway parking lot, crying. A bag boy saw her. Said she didn't know where she had parked or where she was going. The manager called us."

"What happened, Suz?"

"I don't know. I could remember my name, but I could only remember I lived in Los Angeles with my Mama. I knew that wasn't right, but I couldn't remember any other house. I was so scared!"

Suzanne was shaking. Maggie turned to the officer. "Where's her car?"

The officer handed Maggie the two grocery bags. "It's probably in the parking lot ma'am. We found this address in her purse and brought her here. Does she have these spells often?"

"No, never before," although Maggie knew she was lying. What she really meant was never this serious, but lots and lots of little episodes.

After that, they shopped together. When they were in the house she checked on Suz as discreetly as she could, making sure the fire under the pans on the stove wasn't turned on and forgotten and that the dog was brought in at night.

126

It was almost a year later when Maggie, needing to be away for a few hours, was unable to find an available friend to stay with Suzanne. She and Suz had talked about Maggie's upcoming absence and Maggie had written down reminders, including notes on each door that said: *Stop! Suz Must Wait Here For Maggie!*

Suz was happy with the arrangement, repeating over and over, "I promise."

When Maggie returned she found Suz still at home, but she was in tears in front of the big mirror that hung over the living room fireplace.

"Get her out! Please get her out!"

"Who, Suz? Get who out of where?"

"Mama! See her? See her in there? I talked to her, but I can't get her out. She's stuck!"

"It's a mirror, honey. There's no one in there. Your mama's not in there. She died, remember?"

"Dead? Mama's dead?" This was clearly new and terrible information, and Maggie immediately regretted she had said it.

"Oh no! Mama's dead and they have her locked up in there. Get her out, Maggie. Mama! Mama!"

Maggie reasoned with her for over twenty minutes. Finally, in desperation, she draped a sheet over the mirror. "She's out now," and Suzanne echoed, "She out."

Two days later Suzanne removed the sheet and they went through the same litany until Maggie replaced the sheet. The day after that Suzanne went past the *Stop* sign on the front door and disappeared. Maggie found her an hour later, miles away, walking to "my Girl Scout meeting." Maggie had additional locks installed and carried the keys around on her belt. She began to feel like a warden.

Afternoons and evenings were better. Once Maggie put away her day's work, Suzanne was there, ready to help with whatever needed to be done. She put the plates and forks that Maggie handed to her on the table, folded each towel as Maggie pulled it from the dryer, and dusted all the dustable and non-dustable surfaces. Maggie learned she must pay attention here as well, after the evening when Suzanne used a full can of dusting spray on the upholstered sofa. Sometimes as they worked together they sang the old songs they both grew up with, and Suzanne remembered more of the words than Maggie did. At those

127

times, Maggie would pretend Suzanne's disease was going away, but then something would happen to bring her back to reality. Friends tried to help by providing transportation, locating resources, and lobbying for respite care, but Maggie could only hold Suzanne closer as the disease took her further away.

Nighttime was the best and the worst. They would lie together in bed, Suz curled like a soft kitten within Maggie's arms, and Maggie would feel her love for this woman and their time together filling her entire body. She held onto each remaining day, trying to memorize every sight and sound and feel and smell of Suzanne, as if her senses were a savings account.

One night while she was in a deeper than usual sleep something woke her. She reached out for Suz and her hand fell onto the coldness of the sheet. She sat up, turned on the light, and called out, "Suzanne!" There was no answer. She went into the bathroom, but it was empty. Grabbing her robe, she started through the house. Suzanne had to be inside since all the doors were locked. Maggie checked bedrooms as she went down the hall. As soon as she entered the living room she smelled the wet cold air. The breeze on her face was damp from rain blowing through the open window. Maggie ran back into the bedroom to pull the keys from beneath her pillow, then back to open the front door. As she went out she began to call, "Suzanne! Suzanne!"

A movement at the end of the street caught her eye, and she ran in that direction, "Suzanne! Suzanne!"

The movement stopped for a moment, then continued. "Kitty, Kitty," Suzanne's voice called.

"Suzanne!"

She didn't stop.

"I have the kitty," Maggie said and Suzanne turned toward her.

"Promise?"

"Come with me, Suz. I put the kitty in the living room." Maggie hoped that by the time they got home Suzanne would have forgotten. The cat she was looking for hadn't been around in fifty years. Although Suz had raised kittens as a child, Maggie was allergic to cats, so the two of them had always had a dog. "Here's Sammy," Maggie said as they went inside. The warm wet tongue on Suzanne's cold wet face caused her to refocus on this newest of the Shelties who, male or female, had all been named Sam.

The next day Maggie put nails into each window frame so none would open wide enough for Suz to escape.

Maggie found she was sleeping lightly while Suzanne prowled at night, rattling dishes and pans, running water to fill a then forgotten bathtub, or boiling water for tea that she did not fix until the shrill shriek of the kettle summoned Maggie, who would fix them each a cup. Maggie was exhausted. She began to experience chest pains, and when she went to the doctor, he told her there was a problem. Nothing short of the vision of herself face down on the floor leaving Suzanne alone and frightened in a locked house could have convinced her to call the "Home." Certainly not her friends, who had been gently and sometimes not so gently, telling her for months that the situation was out of control.

* * *

Suzanne adjusted well to her new life in the Home. Maggie on the other hand cried nightly for months. While Maggie tossed in the bed that now felt too big, Suzanne chatted away in her emerging nonsense language with the night staff, who allowed her to roam within the secure environment of the Home to her heart's content. She was safe and cared for, while Maggie felt the isolation and loneliness like a cold shroud.

The difference came without warning. Maggie arrived that night at the Home after dinner. The evening was still warm, and Suzanne was sitting in the garden, seeing each flower over and over as if for the first time. She looked up as Maggie joined her and Maggie saw recognition in her eyes. As Maggie reached out to take her hand, there was a moment of lucidity when Suz said, "Let's go to the beach."

"Yes," Maggie answered. "We'll go tomorrow. Would you like that?"

But the moment had already passed and Suz was gone again, leaving Maggie to hold the hand of this body who physically resembled the woman she had loved for her whole lifetime. Maggie held her gently, hoping for another lucid moment. "Tomorrow, Suzanne, we'll go to the beach."

That night she stayed until bedtime. Suz seemed tired and Maggie thought she might even sleep through the night for a change. She helped Suz change into her nightclothes, brush her teeth, and comb out her long hair that was still blond. "The ravages of time are different for each of us," Maggie thought. "I wish Suz had terrible wrinkles and white hair instead of this. But maybe...."

"Tomorrow," Maggie said again. "We'll go to the beach tomorrow. And you'll get better, won't you? Promise?" Suzanne had echoed "Promise."

They called Maggie at midnight to tell her that Suzanne had died.

"No!" Maggie cried. "She knew me tonight. She was getting better!"

No amount of explanation or reassurance helped, although friends continued to try. "Give yourself time," they said. "Time will help. We promise. You have to wait."

The next day Maggie went to the beach and the next and the day after that. Today, in an hour, Suzanne's ashes would be scattered.

"Let's go to the beach," Suzanne had said.

"Time will help," her friends had said.

Now, on the cliff above, the friends waited. Below, on the beach, Maggie waited. By the water's edge, a small sand bird waited, watching the water recede so it could grab a portion of its dinner. Only the pulsing ocean and the screaming gulls refused to wait.

THE NURSING HOME
J. David Nightingale

She was sitting near two others and her face lit up in recognition.

"David!" she cried.

A Christmas tree stood in an alcove; cards on the TV; streamers and decorations across the walls.

"David!" What a surprise!"

"I said I'd come. I sent two cards. Didn't you get them?"

"No."

"O she did," said the matron who had ushered me in and was bringing me a cup of tea. "You said no sugar, right?"

"I didn't get ONE CARD," said mother. "Now – what a surprise. Where are you?"

"I'm here mother."

"What boy?"

"I'm here with you."

"Ah no, I don't think so. Where have you come from?"

"The airport. I drove straight here. I didn't get any sleep on the plane, and pretty soon I'll go and get a good night's rest."

"O no, so soon?"

"I'll be back tomorrow, I promise."

"I must make tea."

"Mother – matron gave me a cup – look."

A lady who looked between seventy-five and eighty-five and with an obvious wig hobbled quickly from the other side of the room and plonked herself down in an armchair.

"Hallo! Have you come far?"

"New York."

"O my! That is far, isn't it?" She began to chuckle. "I'll introduce myself, if you don't mind. I'm Mrs. Saunders. I know your mother. And it is nice to see a visitor here."

"PUT THAT DOWN! LEAVE THOSE ALONE!"

131

A white-haired woman was shaking her cane at a doddery patient who was attempting to clear away coffee cups from a central table of flowers.

"O YOU FOOL, PUT THEM DOWN," the stern-faced cane woman ordered again. A cup and saucer hung precariously at forty-five degrees. The doddery woman, knees slightly bent, stared at the pointing cane. Matron had left, but a girl in a blue uniform came in and caught the cup, gently leading the frail woman to her chair.

"Come on dear, sit over here."

"That's what goes on," said mother.

Mrs. Saunders interrupted: "Your mother's such a nice woman – a real lady. We wish we could talk to her; such a shame really. I used to be a nurse; I've seen it before. This is a terrible place, you know. O yes. I've seen my attorney and I'm not staying here. Just up the road there are two wonderful places – not like this. My lawyer, she's taking me there to see them again tomorrow."

"Who's that?" asked mother.

"It's Mrs. Saunders. She's telling me about nursing homes."

"I thought you came to see me. I don't know her."

"You know Mrs. Saunders – she lives here with you."

"Hallo dear," said Mrs. Saunders.

"No. It's not my line," said mother. "Now will you have some tea?"

"I have some. It's right here in my hand."

"No I mean, I must give them a call."

"Who mother?"

"Who?"

"Who must you call?"

"Call?"

"Yes, you said you must give them a call."

"O, I don't know at all. Now let's walk the dog."

Mrs. Saunders began to chuckle. "O you must excuse me laughing. It's so sad. Mother's not always confused, you know."

The young girl came in again – plain, energetic, cheerful.

"Will you join us for supper – we have plenty."

"I'm very tired. Could I accept for tomorrow?"

"Yes, of course – any day."

The year before I had hurried away from her cottage in shock, knowing she couldn't go on like that. The sons who had been exiled to boarding school by the age of seven had this year exiled their own mother. She had lived independently until the age of eighty, when complaints had been received from the neighbors that she was walking the dog across Rusthall Common in her underclothes, and that smoke had been seen billowing from the kitchen. One neighbor had mended her toaster five times, and he had once found a fork jammed inside the element. The same neighbor had perfected climbing through her upstairs landing window on the many occasions she had locked herself out. And that year I found her with the dog bones in the refrigerator and her own groceries in the oven. The normally spotless and polished dining room table was littered with unpaid mortgage slips, TV rental, electricity, taxes, advertisements, magazines, plates of dried eggs, and threatening notices of curtailment of services. Her husband had died fourteen years earlier and her only company in the cottage had been the ugly terrier-like mongrel watchdog that dozed on the radiators or barked murderously at passersby. But here in the nursing home the patients are her new family, and I shudder at many things including the thought of my own passing years. The vicar had let slip a non-positive reference on the home, and I worried we were making a bad mistake. Yet one of the girls had come in and sat for an hour with her arm around the doddery one, rocking gently, saying nothing, just holding her.

* * *

Sitting motionless, with her eyes closed in what seemed like endless sleep, was someone who had lived all her life in China. Her head of clean white hair was sunk into a bony shoulder, but her face portrayed dignity and something else. Perhaps as a younger person she had been vivacious and beautiful – perhaps she had played a part in modern Chinese history, the revolution for example. Perhaps she had been an ambassador's wife. Perhaps she had been a writer or poet – perhaps none of it. Who was she? Maybe she had been the spinster sister of someone working there. No one knew, for she never said a word, and if any of the

133

girls spoke to her, she would just look up with her big brown eyes and wait expectantly.

* * *

"Tea-time!"

Mrs. Saunders, Miss Law ("It's the Law!" had cried Mrs. Saunders of the ninety-year-old spinster with the huge head) and Mrs. Hillary (a forgetful youngster of seventy who still walked every day) sat at one table. Mother and I and Mrs. Pyatt sat at another, and at the third, poor Mrs. Doddery had to put up with the critical, stern-faced woman-with-cane, and Mrs. "Manchester," and an unnamed deaf woman.

"Mr. Mitchell will be joining you," the girl who was serving the Welsh rarebit said to me. "C'mon, Bert!"

An old man in a suit stood at the door. Short, square-jawed, white-haired, a watch-chain hanging from his waistcoat, but unshaven for a week or so, he hesitated, surveying the eaters.

"Come on and sit here. We have two men with us today."

"O all right."

He sat next to mother and ate a mouthful.

"How d'you do Mr. Mitchell," I said, wondering whether I should say anything or whether he preferred quiet.

"O all right I suppose." Then he raised his voice. "But these bloody women! I can't STAND THEM!" He began to struggle up from the chair he had occupied for all of three minutes. "THEY'RE ALL CRAZY!" he yelled. One of the girls came from the kitchen, but he wouldn't sit down again.

"I hope it wasn't me," I said as she passed by.

"O no. He's often like this. I'll give him tea in his own room."

"I'm from Munchester! Where you from luv?" came a voice from the third table.

Mrs. Saunders told her. Then again,

"I'm from Munchester!"

"Yes, yes, I got that dear," said Mrs. Saunders. "But what about your family? Do you have family?"

"Eh?"

"A family, dear. Sons and daughters – do you have any sons and daughters?"

"I'm from Munchester!"

"Yes, I know that," said Mrs. Saunders, giggling. "You already told me that. But I was asking if you have a family."

"From Munchester. Where you from luv?"

* * *

Clutching the railings of the steps, mother reached the gate of the nursing home. My rental car was parked a few feet away and I opened the door and slipped the absorbent plastic-undersided square onto the upholstery of the passenger seat. Prim, the nurse who had packaged us off, had said, "She'll be safe. She has a big diaper on."

Mother wanted the car door to open from the front, hinges on the back. She would not walk past the door so as to get in.

"I should still have my car," she said. Eventually I got her sitting, but one leg was still outside.

"Let's have the other foot in, mother,"

"Can't we go like this?"

"It may not be legal."

"I bet it is," she replied.

"Please mother, put your foot in, then I can close the door."

"It IS in!"

"No, the one that's still on the curb."

The leg did not move. I tapped her old brown leather shoe and tried to guide it into the passenger well.

"What are you doing?" she asked.

Ultimately we got going. I took her to the South Downs where she and my father had often walked. She did not get out of the car. On the way back I asked her if she remembered my father's name.

"O now, that's a difficult one," she said. I listed some names. At Gordon she said, "Yes, that's it, Gordon."

I asked the 1925 graduate of London University: "What is four plus three?"

"O dear, I don't know."

* * *

On a mild afternoon we went to visit father's grave. Parked outside the lychgate of the Norman church, we started up the pathway between tombstones and grassy banks. Inside the church would be the embroidered tapestries she had done twenty-five, fifteen, and ten years ago. After a few steps she stopped.

"These," she said. "Let's go here." She was pulling the diaper down.

"I think it should be up, mother." She wouldn't go on. She wanted the diaper down, and she wanted to get off the path.

We walked another three paces. Then she was shoving it down again, and the diaper appeared like a bag at the hem of her skirt. It looked clean and I attempted to pull it up. Father's grave was behind the church, and we hadn't yet reached the front of the building. Every few steps, she pulled the diaper down and I pulled it up.

When we reached the church walls she clung to the buttresses and stones while I held her under the armpit. Four years ago she had driven herself here every week to place flowers, and now I realized I had not done her a favor by bringing her out. We reached the small stone cross and looked down at the black lettering: "Gordon Wallis Nightingale, Honorary Canon of Rochester, 1906-1968."

"O yes," she said. "Gordon looks all right. I must drive the dog to tea next week."

* * *

"Will you be staying again this evening?" inquired matron.

"Thank you, yes."

"Good, fine, our meal will be 5:15 today, as usual," and she walked briskly away. Mrs. Saunders said, chuckling, "That's good. That means it'll be edible!"

"Really?"

"Yes, they put on something special if there are visitors you know. O yes, you bet your life on it. Sometimes the food is terrible here."

Holding one of those card advertisements that fall from the pages of magazines, mother said:

"Gordon's desk...they're all buried. When we saw his grave the other day...these things (points to the advertisement for a hardware store) should be buried with him."

"What's the leaflet mother?"

"O plumber...and repair. Now shall I make some tea?"

"You said, shall I make tea?"

"What? I don't remember saying anything like that, but still, if I got a bucket I could catch it!"

"Catch what?"

"No, I don't actually have anything to do with the Langton Post Office...who's got a car?"

She began unfastening her shoe.

"Why are you taking your shoe off mother?"

"I'm not."

She completed the unfastening and kicked it off.

"Now those don't look overdone," she said. Then pointing to some magazines: "...small books. Other than a book, shall we go out for a walk?"

"We could, but it's snowing."

"Do you remember when Michael first went to Canada?"

"Yes."

"He used one of these armchairs – Berkeley or whatever it is – I feel I've just been pushed into one and that's that."

I knew what she was saying, and my brother and I had each agonized over the alternatives.

"How would you like some Kit Kat?" I asked, taking the bar I had brought for her from my pocket.

"I like Kit Kat, I always have done...I tried to get hold of Michael last night – I couldn't – the phone was not working properly."

"Why?"

"Probably he had something else to do. I must admit...however kind one is, you can't get over that feeling of knowing what to do next...it is a makepiece do..."

"What is?"

"Adopting it as my husband."

"What do you mean?"

"You mean – keeping this place clean? Well, that's your ordinary housework, isn't it?"

"Mother, I know you don't like everything here. Would you prefer to be somewhere else?"

"I would prefer to be in my own place. It's simply arduous work. There's a piece of chocolate. At any rate you can write letters here."

I said nothing for a while. I was indeed writing. Thinking that little had been remembered, I asked:

"So mother, how do you feel today?"

"O, I feel moderately all right. But nothing will come up to escorting the other cottage I had. You spent most of your growing up days there." (I didn't. My brother and I began buying the cottage for her after I was married and had two children.)

"I didn't think it was right to take the shoes out. And so, we must go to the bank. It's no good; I can't get sense into it..."

* * *

The lady from China had her eyes open and her head straight. She was looking directly at me, smiling. Then her eyes faltered, fluttered, and she looked down again. Matron came to announce supper. As we filed slowly out of the living room, I received another warm smile.

* * *

It was my last supper at the home, and I had refrained from telling mother until that afternoon. If I had told her before, she would have asked every day if it was my last.

Mr. Mitchell had joined us again and was eating his soup. At the end table the stern-faced cane-woman was saying to Mrs. Doddery: "O YOU FOOL! YOU ALREADY HAVE A SANDWICH ON YOUR PLATE! DON'T TAKE A SECOND ONE TILL YOU'VE EATEN THE FIRST! WHAT DISGUSTING MANNERS!" At the third table Mrs. Saunders was uncharacteristically accusing Mrs. Law of not minding her own business. Mrs. Hillary turned to my table and asked:

"When are you leaving? Is it tomorrow you said?"

"Yes, tomorrow."

"Where will you be going to?"

"New York."

A moaning came from upstairs, a loud slow cry of pain. It was Eva, who was dying of brain cancer.

"She's sounding like an owl today," observed Mrs. Law. "Like a hoot owl."

Mrs. Hillary asked: "Where are you going tomorrow?"

"New York."

"Oh yes, you said that didn't you. I'm so sorry."

Mother was holding her spoonful of tomato soup near her mouth, as if she imagined it was too hot.

"Eat it, for goodness sake," said Mr. Mitchell. He pushed the spoon closer to her mouth.

"That's what I have to put up with," mother said.

Mrs. Hillary turned to me again and said, "Where are you going?"

"New York," I replied quickly, remembering painfully the times I had absentmindedly asked my wife the same question twice over.

* * *

The jumbo with four hundred people surged into fifty mile an hour winds and rain clouds, bumping its way above the weather. When the blue sky emerged, I made my way to the bathroom. Coming out of the bathroom, I was confused by the knobs on the door. Worse, I forgot how far up my seat was. In terror, I wondered if confusion came from a virus.

In my coat pocket was a bundle of photos, one of which my cousin had given me. It was of a young bridesmaid at my uncle's wedding – pretty brown curls, smart figure, bright eyes, delicate shoes, and white dress.

Although mother denied it, it was in fact her.

MOTHER-IN-LAW
Donna Pucciani

Don't get me wrong; this is not a sentimental poem.
My mother-in-law died a year and a half ago,
witless as the day she was born,
and things are different now.

Peter flew over to England, dark-suited and serious,
to give the eulogy, the usual heartwarming stuff
about five brothers and a sister, poor-but-happy,
wearing all hand-me-downs,
father working overtime on the buses,
mother perennially at the stove for the morning fry-up.

Through the years she puffed to Burnage Lane
to buy chops of Welsh lamb, tins of beans,
her collar up against the damp,
her flesh-coloured stockings holding back popping-blue
veins
until, finally, panting over the threshold,
she'd lay her parcels down
and put the kettle on for tea.

Do you know what I mean
when I say it is not the same now?
All mother-in-law jokes aside,
to bathe her those last days
before the hospital, the nursing home,
bearing her sharp odours on fresh summer mornings,
was unbearable,
the gradual goneness of her, the vague daily humiliations,
the receding line of understanding,
the non-recognition behind those sloping, gray doe-eyes
filled with hidden grace.

THE FUNERAL PARLOR
Helen Resneck-Sannes

We enter the funeral parlor. The room is dimly lit and we can barely read a sign that says: *Please Sit On The Couch.* There are two long leather couches. None of us move toward them. I look up and notice the ceiling is high with deep texturing. There are raised areas in the room underneath a round dome in the ceiling. I taught in a room like that in Toronto last year. It was a chapel and whenever I stood beneath the raised part of the ceiling, my voice echoed and I felt like God talking. We stare at the couches for a while longer and then a man ushers us into another room. Although he is quite a bit younger than the four of us, his dark suit and starched white shirt give him an air of authority. He introduces himself as Mr. Dumstead and sits down behind an enormous desk. It is spotless and empty, without even one piece of paper on it.

Janet quips: "Behind in your paper work?"

This room is also dimly lit and there is one couch with two chairs near his desk. Janet, Dusty, and I sit on the couch while Billy, the eldest brother, takes a seat near the desk. Dad has died, which ends the Conservatorship. Bill has been appointed executor of Dad's estate, so he is now in control of the finances.

"I guess I'm up at bat next," he says.

"Yay," I yell, and then I realize my enthusiasm is unsettling to everyone at that moment, so I explain myself. "I'm sorry Dad died, but I have to say, I am grateful to be released from this Conservatorship and his 300 accounts."

Mr. Dumstead clears his throat and begins. "I have some questions that by law I'm required to ask. First, I want you to know that there are four crematoriums available. They all do the same thing. One has a bad reputation, so it is cheapest. The other two cremate a small volume of bodies and are the most expensive. Finally, there is one in Marin. Marin County has a lot of cremations so this makes it cheaper."

"Is that kind of like the Wal-Mart of crematoriums?"

"Yes," he says and smiles. I see that he is able to appreciate our humor and not hold a posture of grief-stricken seriousness. "You could describe it like that and by the way, call me Jerry."

"That's the one I think my dad would like," I tell him and my brothers agree. Jerry writes some things down on a piece of paper that he's retrieved from the top desk drawer. "OK, next," he says, "There is the question of how your dad is to be transported to the crematorium. We used to transport everyone in cardboard, but now there are regulations and you have several options. We have a cardboard box, a pine box, an oak box...."

Dusty interrupts. "The cheapest. We want cardboard."

"No," Janet protests. "You can't send him in a cardboard box."

"I think I'm with Dusty on this," I say.

Billy nods his head and says: "Me too."

Janet is horrified. "You can't."

"Actually," I say, "I think my dad would really like 'the boys' (my brothers) to pick up his body and put it in the back of Dusty's truck and drive him to the crematorium in order to save money."

"He'd have me out looking for a refrigerator box right now to put him in," says Dusty.

"So, it's cardboard," says Jerry.

Janet's face gathers itself into a mockery of worry. "I don't know if I can forgive you guys for this. This is like going to the funeral parlor with Woody Allen's family."

Jerry begins to read from a piece of paper. "You need to be aware that all of your father's gold fillings, jewelry, clothes, any items he now is wearing will be cremated with him."

No wonder Jews were against cremation after the holocaust. I have a vision in black and white. Men in gray cotton suits are picking out the gold from the teeth of corpses. Large smokestacks loom in the distance against a gray drizzly sky. I quickly push that picture away and think about my dad.

"I don't think the shirt he is wearing is his shirt," I say, still trying to remove the bleak images.

"Yes it is," says Dusty. "Don't you remember the blue shirt with the bear on it?"

"I don't think he ever had a shirt like that."

Mr. Dumstead says, "It happens. Once we had a funeral for a lady. Her things arrived from the nursing home, including a little embroidered pillow. Written on it in silk thread was the sentence: 'We love you Grandma.' Someone saw the pillow in her casket during the funeral and was horrified. She never had any children."

Everyone is quiet for a few minutes. I break the silence.

"I know this is weird, but I have one other request. I want something of mine to be cremated with Dad."

"What is it?" Billy asks.

"This is not a well thought out decision. When I received the call last night that Dad was dying, I packed everything in a hurry. All I have is an old triathlon shirt." I hold up the shirt.

"Can she do that?" Dusty asks.

"Sure, let me tell you another story." Jerry begins. "One time a man wanted to bury a can of beer with his grandfather. When he was 10 years old his grandfather had caught him drinking beer. Instead of telling his parents, he had sat down with him, shared the beer, and talked to him about the problems associated with drinking. So, he placed a beer in his grandpa's casket. During the funeral as they lifted the casket, they heard this clank pop pow, and beer began oozing out the sides of the casket. Needless to say, the mourners were quite frightened."

"Do you want to put something in with your dad?" Janet asks Dusty.

"No that's okay." He gives me that, "I've got a weird sister" look.

Now it's time for the "viewing of the body." I want to touch him and stroke his cheek one last time. Janet warns me. "Helen, this isn't going to be like you think it is. He has been in a cold room overnight. He may not feel like you think he will."

"I hear you. I get that it might be hard for me. Thanks."

* * *

Dad is stretched out on a table, his eyes closed. He is wearing the blue shirt with a little bear on the left. My dad's face was always alive with animation and movement. His face is still and the skin is tight, emphasizing his prominent cheekbones and aquiline nose. He looks regal. I stroke his hands and feel his soft skin. I outline the bones of his cheeks, as if to memorize with touch and vision this face I have known all my life and will never see or touch again.

After the others leave and I am alone with him, I pry one eyelid open to see if his eyes are still the same intense blue as when he was in the hospital. They have returned to their gray blue softness. I pass my hand near the top of his head and feel a slight warmth. I wonder if it is like the Tibetans say, that it takes awhile for the soul to leave the body and find its way out of the top of the head.

Soft crying sounds emerge from my mouth. Slowly, the sounds begin to change and gather up into a full wail of rage. I am surprised at my own reaction. I will not allow myself to scream. I think I should be relieved that he is free from pain, but I am angry that he is gone. I want to see the smile that lights up his eyes as I enter the room.

* * *

We return to Dusty's house and he and Billy set out a bottle of vodka and tomato juice. I bring up the topic of the funeral. We decide that we will have a service in Petaluma. I think that we should also have a service in Marion, where he lived the last 60 years of his life. I wonder if Dusty and Billy are interested in coming.

Billy announces loudly: "I'm not going to Marion."

"You're not?" says Dusty astonished.

"I'm only asking who might want to come." I am surprised that my voice sounds so calm. I guess I'm not as shocked as Dusty by Billy's response. I know that he is embarrassed by Dad's behavior in Marion and doesn't want to be bothered with a difficult and expensive plane flight. It costs more to fly to Marion, Indiana than to Paris, France.

Billy looks at me and says that he will think about it.

Dusty brings out bagels and cream cheese. He reaches into the cream cheese container with his fingers. I'm about to ask him to use a knife and then I realize that it's his house and our father just died, so it shouldn't matter.

144

"You know," begins Bill. "Dad really doesn't want a funeral. When I was in Marion last time at the gravesite, he told me to sneak in and dig up the place next to Mom and bury him myself."

Dusty licks his fingers and is about to put them back into the cream cheese when I pull it away. "That sounds like one of Dad's good ideas. Was that before or after the Alzheimer's?"

Dusty yells, "What are you doing?"

"Use a knife."

Billy pours himself another drink and continues, "That was the problem. He was so quirky, how could you tell? You all remember Mr. King, Dad's janitor at the store? I went down to the basement once and Dad was on the ladder and Mr. King was watching while he changed the light bulbs."

"Do you remember," adds Dusty, "when we tried to lift the desk with Mr. King and all four of us couldn't do it. Then we looked down and Mr. King had his foot on the bottom. It was too heavy because he was standing on it."

I also refill my glass and add, "Sounds like Mr. King and Dad were a good match. What I could never figure out is how he knew if someone came near his top dresser drawer. He stowed little plastic toys for us in between his socks. Sometimes I carefully opened the drawer, looked at the contents, and then shut it. I didn't touch a thing, and yet when he came home from work, he would ask: 'Who was in my dresser drawer?'"

Dusty finishes off the last of the bagels and closes up the cream cheese. "Do you think he had it jerry-rigged?

"How would he do that?" I ask.

Dusty stands by the porch door. "He could have put a little piece of paper on the drawer and it would have fallen if anyone opened it."

I can't imagine that he would have gone to all that trouble. "Do you think he would have done that?"

Billy and Dusty look at each other and laugh at me. Dusty is almost out the door as he says, "Let's go for a walk."

"Wait," I yell, "I need shoes." Dusty has already started slowly up the hill. I slip on my shoes and run after him. We slow down to allow Billy and Janet time to catch up. The sun slowly and gracefully lies down on the hills below.

145

On the opposite side the moon begins to rise. It is an enormous red ball that looks too heavy to ever rise up in the sky. It seems to grow out of the hills. It is the night of the full moon in Libra, the time when the moon and sun are in balance with one another.

MISSING ITEMS
Zelda E. Segal

When Sooky entered the house, a single, cool shaft of air brushed her face and a surprising ray of sunlight warmed her, as if Leo were home. But Leo wasn't home. That morning, an ambulance had carried Leo, wrapped in a white blanket, to the hospital, Sooky hovering beside him within the siren's enclosing whine. Hours later Jim and Ida, her two neighbors, drove her back to the narrow Queens street and her own house in its trim row of small houses.

At the far end of the driveway, three wide, flat, hand-carved ducks, which Leo had chiseled and hung onto the garage door twenty years ago, flew on a graceful angular course. Closer, at the lawn's edge, filled to the brim with pumpkin seeds and peanut butter, stood a weathered feeder. Two nuthatches perched on its ledge and nibbled. From the same post, like a flag in the wind, dangled a carved sign with red letters and a white flying duck in the corner – another product of Leo's inventiveness. *The Cooperman's*, the sign said.

Jim and Ida waved from their maroon Chevrolet parked at the curb. Sooky was a small, plump figure in a black coat waving back. After she was safely behind her closed door, she heard Jim and Ida drive away.

At first, Sooky noticed several gray rags and a strange, unfamiliar grouping of magazines on the carpet. Then on the table in the dining nook, she saw a pair of woolen gloves and some tools, Leo's tools. She wondered why they were there. She had forgotten her gloves, surely forgotten everything that morning in the stark turmoil that began when Leo lowered his head between his knees in the bathroom and grunted inaudibly. After that, Sooky's awareness of Leo's slightest movements sharpened to a razor's edge – his heaving toward the towel rack or grasping

147

for the washcloth – and his smallest sounds, husky gurgles, as he stumbled, hot with fever, back to bed.

Though sometimes forgetful, her Leo wasn't an old man. It didn't seem possible that he was 77 and she was 75. She tried never to think about their ages. They never felt old. She recalled the morning about six weeks ago when, lifting the bedroom blind to let the summer sun stream in, Leo pronounced with the glee of a boy, "What a glorious day, Sooky. Let's drive up to the lake and do some canoeing." They had loaded the car with sweaters and the picnic cooler, headed leisurely out toward a Jersey park, whiled away an hour on the water and dragged the canoe up the muddy bank, laughing and puffing.

And wasn't it less than a month since that business about the leak in the roof: "Now honey, don't worry. I can repair it myself. I just need to climb up this ladder for a little look at the problem." Oh no, Leo was still her doer, her fixer, her navigator, with the same entrancing smile behind the salt-and-pepper mustache that had captured her affection at Camp Kittitinee fifty years ago.

That was the summer she had changed her name to Sooky. Leo's idea and she remembered the exact moment it happened. They were both leaning against a gray picket fence in a wide-open wheat field, brown and slim in camp whites, when he tickled her nose with a piece of dried grass and said, "You're pert and winsome – hardly a Sara. You're a Sooky!"

* * *

How strange that the terrace door stood ajar, and in October. Had Leo left it open? Had she? She backed away. What were the magazines and newspapers doing strewn on the floor? She gasped and scanned the room. The stereo and turntable were gone. So were the TV and the VCR the children had given them. Oh God! The burglars had returned for the fourth time. But why, with Leo sick and she there all alone?

Her hands dropped rigidly to her sides. Broken glass covered the dining nook floor. Yes, they had smashed the low window again, cruelly trampling the peonies and lilies-of-the-valley as they had three times before.

The alarm! She hadn't turned on the alarm. After the last break-in, they finally purchased and installed one and since then they had never forgotten to turn it on. But this morning Leo had been too weak to speak to her, and when the attendants carried him out on the stretcher, her desolation at being so completely cut off from him had so overwhelmed her that she could think of nothing else. Still, Ida had been there. Oh why hadn't Ida reminded her to turn on the alarm?

Against a living room wall, leaned a small ceramic-topped table that Leo had designed and baked in a kiln at the high school where he used to teach biology. The six tiles, when fitted together, revealed a bouquet of yellow tulips. Sooky had used the table for fruit platters, snacks, and extra serving space at parties. But now...ahhh...she rolled onto the carpet and patted the cracked table's splintered legs. Thank God no tiles were broken. But the legs...he'd replace the legs as soon as he came home. Everything would be as it was. She held the slivers and wedges close, as if comforting an injured child.

* * *

"Stay back, Mrs. Cooperman. I'm going through the house."

The tall, young policeman, whose voice boomed unexpectedly basso like an opera singer's, held two revolvers in his large hands and walked stealthily up the hall and into each bedroom.

"No one's there. The drawers are emptied out all over the floor, Mrs. Cooperman. That's all. You're lucky, there's no damage. Now downstairs."

The officer lumbered away, guns poised. Could the burglars still be waiting in the basement? Had they found the silver Leo stashed away under the boiler?

"You sure are lucky, Mrs. Cooperman. They knocked over a few things, but not too bad. Your husband should check out his tools."

"My husband is in the hospital."

Can you check them then? We need a list by the end of the week. You better go through the house and call your insurance company."

Ida, who had slipped in unnoticed, led Sooky to a chair. There was too much to do. Sooky pushed shards of glass and chunks of mud with her foot. She wished that Leo were here; Leo always took care of everything.

"Look, Mrs. Cooperman," the officer went on. "You should see what they do to other places. They pour insecticides, disinfectants, and acids all over the furniture. They rip the stuffings out of the sofas with their knives, and they throw paint on the carpets and walls. They set fires and trample the fires out. The place gets all black and sooty. God, you've got to be lucky."

Will this brash young man ever leave? Then again, maybe he'll sit outside the front door until morning, when surely Leo will come home.

"Are you all right, Sooky?" Ida said. "Here, dear, let me get you a drink of water." Sooky sipped the water, her head whirling, her eyes burning. "Stay with Harry and me tonight, dear."

After the policeman left, Sooky said she ought to telephone the doctor.

"Why not wait, dear. You're so upset."

"No, I have to. They told me he'd be in intensive care for a short time, and then moved to his own room. I can't visit him except for those three half-hours. I can't even talk to him on the phone."

But the doctor was tied up with a patient and his assistant said he would return her call later.

Just as the officer had said, their underwear, stockings, socks, nightgowns, pajamas, and sweaters were strewn wildly about the bedroom carpet and under the oak bed. Even the contents of their closets had been emptied out like a costumer's warehouse turned upside down.

"Let's just put everything away in case Leo comes home tomorrow," Sooky said. "I don't want him to see this mess. It makes me sick to my stomach to think our clothing was molested by strangers."

"I know, dear. It's awful." Ida exhaled a low moan. "I felt exactly the same way after our break-in."

Sooky realized immediately which pieces of jewelry were missing: her Bulova watch, Leo's Seiko, the silver wedding band with "This Is My Beloved" emblazoned on the outside, two cloisonné necklaces that Leo had created the first year he retired, and some fake gold chains she enjoyed wearing

150

on her sweaters. Ida got a white, legal-sized pad from the guest room and wrote down each item.

They spent an hour sorting through the clothes and jewelry. They refilled the drawers and replaced the trinkets. Her father's 14-karat gold watch fob had been taken the last time, and also her pearl choker, a gift from Leo on their 35th wedding anniversary. And the time before, her mother's diamond ring, which had been hidden inside her underwear, and the tiny heart-shaped locket her mother had worn in grade school. Sooky had folded it in tissue paper and tucked it between the sweaters.

"They take jewelry, Ida, but they never touch the typewriter. They stole my mother's sterling silver coffee pot, my fur jacket, and Leo's camera. Why don't they steal my good linen or the French glassware from Aunt Min? Or this TV?" She pointed to the small Sony on the chest of drawers. "It's a big mystery to me."

"They steal what they can sell for money. That's what they steal," said Ida.

"Why do they keep coming back? Haven't they cleaned us out? It's as if they know us, know what we still have."

In an eerie way, having possessed her personal belongings even momentarily on four different occasions had brought her robbers peculiarly close. The broken window ledge was caked with mud. Dirty tracks led through the shattered glass to the front door where the thoughtful culprits had removed their shoes and tiptoed barefoot into the bedroom. Could they be "the hungry poor?" If so, she wished she could say to each of them, "Keep the 'objects.' Turn them in for cash if that's what you need." But what of the rest? What of the moments and days and years that each item represented? What of her memories of girlhood, growing up, the children, her marriage? With each unseemly break-in – surely part of a grander scheme unknown even to the poachers themselves – thin leaves of Sooky's life were being peeled away with a kind of slight-of-hand, released into the world, then consumed.

Later that night, Sooky reached the doctor.

"He's still in intensive care, Mrs. Cooperman. His temperature is high – over 103. We've got him hooked up to an IV and a Monitor. We're putting him through every kind of test."

When Leo was eight years old, a peanut had become lodged inside his lung, causing an infection. His lung was removed in a painful, nine-hour operation that kept him hospitalized for over a year. Daily, the doctors drained out the pus with a needle the size of the Alaskan pipeline. Should she tell the doctor that Leo had purposely stayed away from hospitals ever since?

"Doctor, when will he get his own room?"

"In the morning. We'll transfer him as soon as a bed opens up."

"It would be so much better if I could be with him, sit with him. Now I can't even call him."

"Yes, I understand, Mrs. Cooperman. Be patient. Tomorrow we'll move him."

Sooky slept badly without Leo. The bed in Ida's pine-paneled guest room was lumpy, and her lower back began to ache. She was awakened by the wind beating through an unopened window, and when she reached for him, she found only a fat, cold pillow, which she clutched panting.

The sun's pink-gray glare seeped in between the blinds. The heat hissed through the vents. She would take him soup and pudding. When he came home, she would show him the list. TVs, VCRs, receipts, and estimates were his department; he had all the files from the last time. Propped up in bed in freshly ironed pajamas, Leo would call the insurance company.

* * *

Sooky learned that Leo was still in the ICU from a woman in a pink and white pinafore. She hurried toward the elevator, leaving Jim and Ida behind in the huge lobby. The sign read: *No One Allowed In The ICU Before The Visiting Period Begins.* She stole in through the door. Four nurses in blue guarded their station. Little white lights in silver machines flickered above their heads.

"I'm sorry, but visitors must wait until twelve o'clock," said one nurse.

I'm Mrs. Cooperman. My husband is not supposed to be here. Doctor Latham told me he'd be in his own room."

The nurse checked the chart. She was heavy, with a round, dimpled face.

"No, he's slated for the ICU. Doctor's orders."

152

"Doctor's orders? There must be some mistake."

The nurse's face was serene; no, more than serene, masked.

"Mrs. Cooperman, I think you should know that your husband became extremely difficult last night. He tore out his IV. We were forced to take him off the monitor. He disturbed the other patients. He got so out-of-hand that we had to place him in a straight jacket."

A straight jacket!

"How is he now?" Sooky replied stupidly.

"He's fine. He listens to me. I have him behaving."

Have him behaving? Never before had Leo "misbehaved."

When she entered his room, Leo was sitting on the edge of the bed eating a small brown hamburger and some applesauce, his white feet dangling below the mobile table.

"How are you, dear?" Sooky whispered. She kissed him.

"I'm fine. Fine. Just bored to death in this place." His white hair floated lightly and glistened. He was pale. "When can I go home?"

"I...I...don't know dear. You'll be getting your own room soon. That will be much better."

"It sure will be better. This is a morgue in here. Look." He pointed with his chin toward the next bed where a man hooked up to tubes and wires lay lifelessly under a white sheet. Up-and-down scribbles beat across a screen above his head. An intravenous tube hung from a pole beside the bed.

"Oh Leo," she laughed. "Be patient, dear. You'll be out of here in a day or two." Leo didn't seem sick – really sick. She noticed blood on the sheet and on his hospital gown. Ought she mention last night's incident?

"Was the doctor in to see you this morning, dear?"

"The doctor? No, he wasn't in. I feel ready to leave this place."

Ready to leave? But why was he still in the ICU? He seemed perfectly fine, perfectly ready – at least for his own room.

"There's blood all over your gown, dear," said Sooky. "How did that happen?"

"I'm not sure. Let's get rid of this thing." He removed the gown and reached for a clean one on the chair. She handed him the gown and helped him into it.

"I've got to get out of here, Sooky. This place is driving me crazy."

She touched his forehead with her lips. His fever had dropped. Why then did the doctor say he would be moved and the nurse tell another story? She reached inside the Bloomingdale's bag she had carried from the car.

"I've got some custard for you, to cheer you up."

"How wonderful. I could use some cheering up. This place is very depressing. I wish I had something to read, like my woodworking magazine."

"The latest issue just arrived; I'll bring it tonight, dear."

*　*　*

Over the phone the doctor spoke crisply, "Mrs. Cooperman, I'm happy to tell you that your husband's tests came out negative. He can go home in a week or so. Maybe sooner, if he regains his strength."

"But why is he still in the ICU, doctor? The nurse told me you ordered it."

"Ordered it? Oh no. We're waiting for a room. I have one now and he'll be moved in today."

"But what about last night?"

"That was pretty difficult. While it was going on, we didn't know the story. We've ruled out everything neurological. Your husband is fine. I examined him myself early this morning. He merely has a very bad virus."

For a flashing second, Sooky recalled that Leo had said the doctor hadn't been to see him. Then she was flooded with delight at the news. "How wonderful. Just a virus? All the neurological tests show he's fine?"

"That's right."

"Then why did he get so upset last night? You know doctor, I didn't tell you before, but Mr. Cooperman hates hospitals. You might say he has a phobia about them." She described Leo's childhood experience.

"Mrs. Cooperman, an event like that could certainly account for what happened. Besides, when a person develops a very high fever, he's frequently unaccountable for his actions. High temperatures frequently cause people to behave irrationally. Rest assured, Mrs. Cooperman, your husband is fine."

"It's sooo good to be home." Leo sighed, dropped onto the sofa, then emitted a wracking cough and covered his mouth. The loose skin on his neck hung a bit lower, his soft, pink hands lay almost fearfully on the cushions. He was obviously still very weak.

Jim carried Leo's suitcase into the bedroom. At seventy, their neighbor, who jogged every morning, was slim and youthful. Only his hands were rugged and gnarled from hard work. Sooky ran to turn off the alarm, which wailed like an ambulance's siren. She decided not to say a word. It was only a question of minutes before Leo would notice. Did he see the window frame edged with dark gray putty? Jim had hammered three boards across the broken window. A few days later, two men replaced the glass and told her not to paint over the putty.

Leo spent the rest of the morning in bed. When he wanted his wristwatch, Sooky handed him the old Timex. He didn't ask about the Seiko, his favorite. The next day after a healthy breakfast, he stood in his plaid wool bathrobe before the living room window. A chickadee and two sparrows scrounged around the middle of the wooden ledge, but gave up. It was empty.

"I'm going to fill the feeder tomorrow, Sooky. The birds need a good breakfast too."

Sooky noticed that when Leo opened the front door to get the paper, he started to step outside, but thought better of it. Why hadn't he mentioned the missing items, the empty spaces, the gaps in the living room that smacked her in the face a hundred times a day? The walnut amplifier and turntable that used to sit on the high shelf, a hole now. And the TV, an enormous 19-inch model no one could miss. She kept wanting to say, "See Leo, the TV's gone." But she waited. She had never kept a secret from him before.

His first week home, Leo didn't get dressed. He wandered about in his robe, finally settling in the bedroom to watch an afternoon soap opera. As the weeks progressed, he became stronger. His cough ceased. He dressed in corduroy trousers and plaid flannel work shorts, his staples. He filled the feeder and raked the yard of dry leaves. He disappeared into his workshop, from where streamed the familiar grinding buzz of the press drill, a sound as necessary to Sooky as eating or breathing.

The police hadn't called. It was a month since Leo had come home and he still hadn't mentioned the missing items or noticed that they were gone. He never asked to play a record or tape a program. When their married daughters called from Cleveland, Sooky told them their father was fine. Only Sooky knew that Leo wasn't fine. She recalled the other break-ins. After each one, he had scurried through his files for receipts. He phoned the police station, the insurance company, the jeweler, and Radio Shack. He reported the losses, discussed the estimates, and made sure the person on the other end knew he was very angry that a bunch of hoodlums had invaded the privacy of his home.

One morning in December, while Leo was napping on the sofa, Sooky, who had come to believe that she could live very well without taped television programs, long-playing records, or a radio, took from her top drawer the list of stolen items that Ida had written down. Holding her slippers in her hand, she tiptoed barefoot to the front door. She stepped into the slippers and gingerly retraced the burglars' steps, as if crossing broken glass, to the dining nook window, which she opened. She glanced over the edge to where the lilies-of-the-valley, trampled four times, lay curled up in hibernating sleep. Carefully, she tore the paper into narrow strips. She gathered the strips together and tore them again until she held in her hand a pile of tiny white pieces. Soon, a sudden rush of snowflakes dropped bewitchingly toward the winter earth, fell slowly, and just as quickly, dissolved.

AFTER THE VISIT OF AN
ELDERLY RELATIVE
Alice Wirth Gray

Smoke pours from behind the stove's
cracker-crisper
where nothing should be. My husband
brings the extinguisher
from the hall and smothers the fire.

We explore and find
a hidden hoard of junk food such as
little plastic cups of soured ice cream
so synthetic it's held its color,
shape and texture
through two unrefrigerated weeks,
and a mummified collection
of my blueberry muffins.

A friend reassures me: his mother
has been found hiding pats of butter
between her mattress and the box springs.
Silently we calculate
how old we are.

COMMUNION
Katie Kingston

My mother dips her fork into the wine glass, brings the empty prongs to her lips, and tastes what little chardonnay, non-alcoholic, has held to the edge of stainless steel. She repeats this ritual three times, then sets the fork down, picks up the pumpernickel and begins to tear it in pieces. After the bread is eaten, she slips the cocktail napkin from under her wine glass and begins to tear it into pieces.

I know she will lift the paper to her lips like the communion, the ritual she had me perform first in a dress of white netting, starched crinoline. *Worthy* was the word the nuns explained to me as I strove for definition, fingers perfectly matched, right against left, white shoes, white socks, a white purse with a white missal and white rosary. My white veil framed my black hair as I walked to the altar, knelt at the rail, tipped my head back, and extended my tongue, flat and patient. I waited for the wafer, careful not to let it touch my teeth, but instead to dissolve at its own pace in the warm palette of my mouth.

Now when my mother lifts the torn cocktail napkin to her lips, I whisper *this is not bread*, as I slip the paper from between her fingers, then replace it with my remnant of pumpernickel, lightly buttered, my heart bears up like a desert outcrop soaking up heat. My voice tells her *this is not bread*. As we finish the last of the non-alcoholic chardonnay, I see our reflections in the tinted glass overlooking the cross-country trails, and lean forward to hold her hand while she names each snowflake as if it were a newborn, one of her eight, slipping from the womb.

This is not bread. I remember how we used to hide these same fingers behind our backs and sing as if each one were a person, *pointer, ringman,* and how I would imitate her hands and let only one finger march forward. *This is not bread.* Then she would recite the alphabet backwards, while I savored the sheer nonsense of sound. My hand stops hers, my fingers pinch the white paper from hers, and I repeat *this is not bread.*

PASSOVER
Stephen M. Fishman

My mother answers the phone at the other end. I say, "You sound better," and she begins to cry. She says he went to the store and became upset when the girl at the register looked at his money twice before making change. He thinks the Secret Service is following him. "I tried to knock his teeth out," she tells me. She is sobbing and apologizing at the same time. "It's comforting to hear your voice," she says.

Some comfort. Seven hundred miles away without answers. That's all I can think of. I say I'm sorry. I mumble about there being good and bad days. She has tried. She has faith. "God must have a reason," she tells me. She cannot abandon her husband now.

She wishes me a "good yomtov" and I remember why I called. A child's obligation. It's the first night of Passover, the Seder. It means nothing to me, but I know she and my father are alone. And did she change the dishes and cover the kitchen counter tops with white shelving paper? What does she feel when she sees the drinking glasses with the decals my brother stuck on when we were kids?

I still don't know what adults think about Passover. To a child it's a crowded dinner table at grandma's. It's cousins home from the Army on leave, and a tall uncle who smells of witch hazel bribing me to eat foreign foods. The words in Hebrew run by me, but all I hear is, "It is to be as if each of us made the journey out of Egypt." It takes me out my grandma's window. I'm in a crowd and doing something simple. Walking. One foot after the other. It is untidy and old, but I cannot deny it; it is a piece of me; it is something to which I belong.

* * *

160

I hear her trying to get my father to come to the phone. She is insisting he say a holiday greeting to his son, no matter how mad his mind has become. I hear her berating him: "Coward! Don't get on the phone! I'll tell him he has no father. No human ignores his own child!" She seems to think if he would just listen to her and understand, he would change. She in turn cannot hear the gloom of the neurologist or the psychiatrist or the family practitioner. They do not speak to her. He will get better. She sees it in small things, small triumphs. Didn't he write that birthday card to Cousin Selma? Didn't he set aside grocery money last week without warning her it was counterfeit?

I hear him on the other end. "Yes," spoken with anger in his voice. Not "Hello." No pretense of normality. What do I say when "yes" means "I don't want to talk to you?" Should I remark about the weather as I usually do? I answer him, "I just wanted to say good yomtov." His response startles me: "I have no one. No one gives a damn about me. I'm all alone."

Quite a change from the way it used to be, huh? I wonder how so much anger got stored up. Was it building, building, all those years? Seventy-seven years of anger?

* * *

Last fall I flew home. Me, the favored son. "Miracle Man." My brother expects me to take care of things. "You take him," he tells me. "You have friends down there. You know people. I can't stand it anymore. He'll abide by what you say." But my father doesn't want me to come. On the phone he begs me not to. Three times I cancel plane reservations. Mom says he's too embarrassed to see me. She thinks it's a sign he knows something is wrong with him. My mother and brother are convinced I can help him, but they keep my coming a secret. My brother picks me up at the airport and we head for their house. I tell him I'm scared. I have a good luck charm in my pocket and confusing stories in my head. He refuses to talk. He's angry about his "burden." If I'm the favored son, I'd better do my magic now.

When we arrive I go upstairs. My mother and brother wait below. Dad is sleeping on my old bed. He looks small and I cannot put all my memories of him into his present

161

shape. I trust to touch, rubbing his back. I put my love into fingertips. Through my fingers I send him all my journeys, all my strength. He wakes up suddenly and gets off the bed. "What are you doing here? What's going on?" He thinks I've come to commit him. He doesn't say so, but I see it in his eyes. I try to hug him, but he moves away and calls for my mom. "I thought I was dead," he says. "Why did you let him come up here? I told him not to come." She responds by telling him that we love him.

In the living room he sits near me and we talk. I answer carefully, trying hard to understand him. I don't know why, but I say, "Think of the word 'happiness' and tell me what you imagine." He smiles and tells me he sees only misery.

"What's wrong with you? Don't tell him that," my mom says, overhearing our conversation from the other room. He mumbles under his breath, bangs his hands on his forehead and whispers, "What should I do? What should I do? Please help me." I don't see him as my father. He's a character actor with wisps of gray hair behind his ears. He's playing the role of a man obsessed by a secret terror in studio clothes several sizes too large and I want to flee.

I ask him, "What are you afraid of?" and he replies, "They're after me. Once the government starts, they hound you until you turn yourself in. You shouldn't have come. Now they'll be after you too."

Again he asks me: "What should I do?" and I try telling him the truth. "You need help." I tell him it's possible he's not thinking clearly and that I've read about drugs that might help him. I get nowhere. It's like our conversations over the phone, only now we both have fewer illusions. "You sound like a psychologist," he answers. "You're naive and too trusting. They're after me. In fact they're filming this. I'm sure of it. I see you don't believe me, nobody believes me, but I was never so sure of anything in my whole life. Never!"

He's in a world I cannot get to. How does my mother take this? Once again she storms at him: What are you saying? Where are the cameras? Where? Where? There's nothing behind the mirrors. I've told him a hundred times. There's nothing."

In the ensuing days I beg her to ask her neighbors for support, to get out and live her own life, but she tells me once her neighbors find out what's wrong, they'll avoid her.

162

Still, when my friend invites me to a birthday party, she agrees to come along. My father is vehement about not going. It's an agonizing show of rhetoric. His arguments go down mineshafts, black whirlpools, and catacomb cul-de-sacs. He is cleverer than both of us. "They'll ransack the house as soon as we leave," he says. "They'll plant more cameras. They'll hire more cars, you'll see." "They" have taken his clothes; "they" have changed the colors of the ones they've left; in the night, "they" have implanted microphones in his teeth. He gives us no rest, no place to hide. At the last minute he realizes we will go without him. He dresses quickly and gets in the car.

It's my friend's fortieth birthday and his wife has an ice cream cake and some funny gifts. We're in the living room when my father leans over and tells me the ginger ale tastes funny. I try to ignore him. I see him working on my mom, and then he's back at me again. "Don't drink the ginger ale," he whispers loudly. "It's poisoned. This is a trap." Later he gets a little sleepy and quiets down. My mom enjoys the party and starts smiling. She even eats some cake. When we're headed for the door he tells me, "I don't want you driving. Let Mom drive. The ginger ale is starting to work on you." I'm angry. I tell him I've known these people for years, and it's preposterous to think they would poison the ginger ale. On the way home he keeps saying, "Doesn't this prove you're wrong? Isn't this evidence that you're not seeing things as they are?" He explains that since he warned me, since he put me on to them, they called it off. They decided not to poison the ginger ale after all.

Later that night, we're upstairs in his bedroom. He asks me how he looks. "Not bad," I say. He smiles and tells me I'm lying. "Just look at me. I'm not a real person anymore. No one walks around like this. I can't face anyone looking like this." I suggest we get some new clothes in the morning. I tell him I've brought extra money with me. He tells me I'm broke. "You weren't home that night when I called because you had to take a second job. You've joined the credit union for the same reason. I know about these things; you can't fool me." Then for the umpteenth time he bangs his head with the heels of his palms and mumbles, "What should I do? What should I do?" I grab his hands and holding them tightly, tell him he needs help. I insist he

163

listen to me. In my mind I'm fighting for my mom, yet somehow I feel I'm proving something else. I'm still scared of him and trying to convince myself I'm not. I'm telling him I'm a real person, that I will not be pushed too far. He looks hard at me, cold black in his eyes, and says slowly "Let go of me. I'm warning you. You'd better let go." I let go. Leaning against the door jam of his bedroom, I break down and cry. I don't know what to do. The favored son is dead. I cannot bring home any prizes. I cannot solve the riddles. I cannot lift the plague. At night, I put my shoetrees against my bedroom door – the once favored son doesn't want to be taken by surprise.

* * *

From the bedroom where I've hung up the phone, I hear my wife call that she's ready to begin the Seder. I come to the table: it's my wife, our two kids, my brother-in-law, and me. My son asks the traditional questions: "Why is this night different from all other nights? On this night, why do we eat only unleavened bread? Why only bitter herbs? Why in a reclining position?" He goes on with answers for the wise son, the contrary son, the simple son, for the son who does not even know how to ask a question. Tonight I am the son who does not even know how to ask a question.

And what about my own son? What do I wish for him? He is seated next to his uncle. Despite thirty years difference in age, they are kindred spirits. My son is in love with his uncle's new sports car. He loves the leather interior, the matching racing mirrors, the bells that announce the seat belt's ajar, like getting ready for an airplane takeoff. My brother-in-law is charming. At 41, he's a bachelor with no steady job, no steady girlfriend, and no steady worries. Today he spent the afternoon waxing his car. When my son kangaroos through the door after school and begs to go shopping, my brother-in-law agrees without hesitation. Later they come home with smiles and trophies, a forty-dollar gift certificate for my daughter and a black leather vest with shiny buttons for my son. When my son laughs, I hear my brother-in-law's laugh. It worries my wife and me. It's the laugh of the drifter, the laugh of the perpetual child.

* * *

Sitting with my head down, I'm privately back at a Seder forty years ago when I sat next to my mother's youngest brother. Tall and thin, he was a hardy man who left school in the sixth grade and ran away from home. Uncle Sam was a fistful of change at the end of a long arm extended down to me. "Pick what you want, Stinky. Go ahead. Aw, don't pick that one, pick the biggest one." When I was twenty he gave me his ring, a silver bulldog with snake eyes. It made me sad that it didn't fit my finger and I couldn't wear it. He had won it playing dice in the streets. By that time, I understood him better, but when I was little he scared me. At weddings he drank too much. At grandma's he was the subject of criticism. In the presence of authority, he exuded confrontation. My father warned my mom: "You watch. Just you watch. Our son'll grow up to be a bum, just like your brother Sam." No, no, I thought. Never like Sam. I'll stay in school and avoid whiskey. I'll stay off the streets and live in libraries. No pinky rings, no cigars, no dyed-hair women for me.

He came on strong. "Let's go Stinky, I'm buying you a new coat." I sensed he was unpredictable and daring. "I'm takin' him to my women," he'd shout at my mom. And she'd protest over his laughter: "Sam, stop that. Sam, what's wrong with you?" I had only a vague notion of what was up, but enough to blush and think of dark gypsy women with long earrings and castanets.

Saturday mornings I'd hold his hand and walk along to the laundry. Since my grandma didn't want anyone in her family working on the Sabbath, he pretended to hide his bundle of shirts under his suit jacket. I was impressed that even my big Uncle Sam thought enough of the rules to pretend he halfway believed them. Once on the way home, he took me to Yoshky's Grocery and bought me two large boxes of Campfire marshmallows. "Your momma's gonna holler at me," he laughed. And for twenty-five years he'd greet me with, "Hey, Stinky, remember what I got ya at Yoshky's?" During the years I was at college, he had one of his women friends send me a cashier's check each month. He never said what it was for, but I knew it wasn't for books. On the day I got married, he took me aside and said,

165

"What are you doin' a fool thing like this for? You're a baby, just a kid. This is gonna kill ya Stinky!"

On his eightieth birthday I was with him for dinner. He carried on in a loud way with the waiter about poor service and the quality of food. Then as if cued by some off-stage producer, he leaned over to me and said he had no regrets. He had had his fun and enjoyed his life. I just shook my head. Although I could have guessed it, I was glad he told me. This way I had no doubts. I saw my father across the table. The paranoia that was to be his had not yet taken over, but anxiety was clear on his face. I could see the worries attacking his mind: Was the car parked on a one-way street that would take us straight to the bridge? How much time was left on the meter? Would we make it home before dark? Would the radio he'd left on in the kitchen keep the vandals out?

Three weeks ago Sam had a heart attack and I called him long distance to see how he was. From his hospital bed he answered, "Grand Central, what's on your mind?" I said, "Hey, Uncle Sam, how are you?" More softly than I thought him capable of, he replied, "You know, Stinky, this call means a great deal to me, more than I can tell you."

* * *

I tune back into our Seder. The Haggadah is alive with rabbis arguing about how many plagues God sent against Pharaoh's soldiers at the Red Sea. They try to explain why we start the service at night and not during the day. I attempt to lose myself in the story, to feel something. It is a night for remembering slavery and escape. It is a commemoration of revolt, of turning against the tide, of fighting the big odds.

The phone rings; I'm certain it's my brother. We're not halfway through our Seder, and he wants to tell me about my responsibilities, to paint a picture that will bring me home and take the burden from his door. When my daughter whispers, "It's your mother," I don't know what to expect. I go to the phone in the bedroom and hear my mom say, "I just wanted you to know we had a Seder, your father and I. Don't worry; it's just that sometimes I get so tired and don't know which way to turn." She moves away from the phone and her voice changes. "I can talk to my son if I

166

want to. I don't care what it costs. Now get out of this room. What'd I tell you? Go on, get out." There's quiet and then she's back on the line. "He's afraid I'll talk about him. He's afraid I'll get two minutes of peace. Listen, listen, I know I'm interrupting. You'd better go back to your Seder."

Sitting on the bed, my head in my hands, I hear my children in the kitchen call out the names of the plagues with which God cursed the pharaoh. They will spill a drop of wine for each one: for darkness, for locusts, for cattle disease, for death of the first born... We are to remember that we marked our doors with the blood of the Pascal lamb. We are to remember that God honored this sign and caused the plagues to pass over us. We are to remember that God took us out of bondage and that our remembering is to be a statute forever. I look at my hands. They ask me a question. "With whose blood may I mark my mother's door?"

THE FORGETTING
Nancy Priff

The Forgetting is coming,
like he came for my mother
and he came for my grandmother.

From the back of our yard, he stalks me,
stares unblinking
to push me off balance.
If I ignore him, I think
he'll go away, leave me alone.
But I'm mistaken.
Whenever my ball of thoughts
lies unattended, he tugs at a loose end,
steals a bit of thread, a scrap of wool
to fashion a small nest.

And I wonder:
Where did I put my keys?
Did I turn off the iron before I left?
What is the name of that actor I like so much?

At night, the Forgetting creeps closer,
takes his place at my back door
like a hobo hoping for a handout.
I threaten him with my heavy black skillet,
"Get away from me or I'll flatten you!"
But he smiles and waits.
I can't make him leave.
And I swear he reaches into my dreams,
pulling out long strings of pearl-gray thoughts
to decorate his growing nest.

And I think:
What day is it?

Where am I supposed to go?
Did I tell you this story before?

Growing bolder, the Forgetting watches
from a corner of my room.
I've given up shouting and throwing things.
It makes no difference.
I use him for a hat rack: he doesn't care.
He simply smiles and waits.
He gathers all but my oldest memories.
weaves them into his strong nest.
"Take whatever you want," I plead,
"but let me remember the people I love."

And I cannot recall:
Did I take my green pill yet?
Did I take that pink pill already?
Did I take this white pill yesterday?

Now the Forgetting follows me close.
But I don't go far, just stay in my room.
He loosens the sunken cables of my thoughts,
winches them out of their murky depths.
When I whimper, he comforts me,
wraps me in a soft cotton bunting
and feeds me on sweet lotus flowers.
On a cushion of fog, I accept the empty nest
he places on my swaddled head –
the lustrous crown of an idiot queen.

And I ask myself:
Who am I?
Where am I?
Do I know you?

WHAT VITA'S MOTHER SAID
Rachael Perry

Vita had no day job. No weekly paycheck or husband. She lived with the round women she made and a mother who couldn't remember her name. Nobody bought her round women, these brilliant ceramics that exploded in oranges and purples, with necks that went on for days and bones that didn't show. They were a "real" size, these round women, with fertile bellies and thick thighs.

When she first created her round women, Vita tried the private museum and the local art gallery – both owned by the same rich, fat man. He didn't want to see her round women and he said others wouldn't pay to see them, either. "Art must celebrate ideals," he told Vita. "Dreams."

She didn't understand this. Vita's dreams were sprigs of wooly hair, long brown eyes, rouge for coloring, not effect. She dreamt of round things – grapefruits, thick silver watches, melons, faux pearly broaches, circles and circles of velvet hats. No shape was more perfect to Vita than a circle – a round union of places she imagined, but had never seen: round, round, full.

After the museum and the art gallery, Vita brought her round women to the Dime Store, to a tourist knick-knack shop, and to the bar-restaurant near the beach. The bartender offered to take them off her hands if she would cut their bellies into ashtrays and this almost made Vita cry.

Later she thought she should have punched him.

* * *

"What's for breakfast, Louisiana?"

It took Vita only a half hour of Alabama, Alaska and Arizona to recognize that her mother recalled the alphabetical list of all fifty states, which she probably learned in the third grade, and she substituted these names when she couldn't think of "Vita." As lists of names went, Vita didn't mind this one so much. She had been cereal ingredients, lines of Latin prayers, and a string of curse words that the younger version of the old woman would've denied ever knowing.

Vita's mother looked the same as she did ten years ago, maybe twenty, with her thick black hair and fine, powdery skin. She wore rumpled jumpers, lots of dirty browns and coffees and toffees, and a terrycloth robe instead of a jacket when she wanted to go outside. If one of her former church friends saw her galloping around the grocery store plucking up packages of canned nacho cheese and cinnamon graham crackers, they might say that Vita's mother was doing just fine. Energetic enough. Perhaps a little thin.

"A feast," Vita said. "Poached eggs, scrambled eggs, eggs over easy, buttered biscuits and marmalade, real bacon not that non-fatty crap, slabs of steak, corned beef and hash, grits, oatmeal, pancakes, waffles with raspberries, and freshly-squeezed orange juice."

"I think I'll have a piece of toast and black coffee, Maine, if you please," Vita's mother said.

Vita's mother asked for this every morning, regardless of any other outstanding offers. A piece of toast and black coffee. A look at the morning newspaper from back to front. A splash of cold water on the face, three dabs with the terrycloth robe to dry. A baking soda tooth brushing and then with remarkable consistency, on to the business of the day. This month, she was engaged in an active search for her childhood dog, Joshua, and two yellow parakeets, Shemp and Curly Joe, who had flown away after Vita's father died.

"The clues are few and far between," Vita's mother had said. "But there are certain things in life you simply cannot not do, Delaware."

If Vita made a list of her own, there would be plenty of things that it seemed she could not do: tuck a shirt into her jeans properly, listen to a country western ballad without tearing up, stop eating once she opened a bag of marshmallows, recognize her own reflection in a storefront window as she passed by with a box of round women under her arm. Instead, she wondered at that round image – is that Vita? – wobbly and salty like a teardrop, which surrounded the broomstick mannequins, overshadowed single-digit dress sizes. Then Vita thought: round! supple! strong! fertile! woman! real! This, at least, she could do.

They spent the mornings together, Vita and her mother. She refused to allow the old woman to wander around alone, for what the police chief would call obvious reasons. So, they walked, sometimes hand in hand, arms swinging like two little girls, sometimes piling their palms and pockets full of shell-etched fossils, chipped arrowheads, sand glass, or other things they found along the way. Their small cottage, wrapped by birches and firs, was on a dusty road less than a mile from Lake Huron. Vita's mother often steered them toward the water, skipped flat stones against rolling mounds of waves, and plopped into the soft sand.

"Look here, Minnesota," Vita's mother said, pointing to a half-rotted trout carcass flopped onto the beach. "Evidence."

And there was evidence, Vita admitted. Dozens of tiny bird-claw footprints twittered about the dead fish.

"Ma, how do you know that was Curly Joe and Shemp? Are you sure those prints aren't from the seagulls?"

"Mississippi, you are the only person I know that can look a cat right in the face and call it a duck."

Vita admitted that her mother had evidence for this, too. The length and depth of most of her relationships could be measured in inches.

"OK," Vita said.

Her mother stripped off her tennis shoes and cotton socks and waddled around the sand in an attempt to pick up the scent. "Is this what girlhood looks like?" Vita wondered. "Is this what we all come back to?" Throughout her life, the mother had lied about her age, and now she couldn't call it truthfully, even if she wanted to. 71? 75? Vita knew she was a miracle of an aged and near-hopeless womb; her mother had never been pregnant and she figured menopause had come a bit early. Instead, it was Vita.

"What are you looking for now, Ma?" Vita called out to the scrawny speck of maroon edging further and further away from her on the shoreline. "Ma?"

But the old woman was bent over, sniffing last night's campfire logs and splashing her bare feet in icy water. She didn't respond.

172

* * *

When they returned from their walk, Clementine was there, as always, cross-legged on their doorstep with fists full of daisies, Rose of Sharon twigs, and freshly snipped cattails.

Clementine: an 80-year-old with a voice like a record player who took pictures of himself flexing in boxer shorts and a ribbed, sleeveless T-shirt for Vita's mom to pin up on her wall. His civilian clothes consisted of one pair of blue jeans, one red flannel, and seven pairs of suspenders, which he rotated each weekday.

While Vita's mother went to fetch her terrycloth robe, Vita said: "Try to get her to eat a cheeseburger, Clem. Or some chili cheese fries and a vanilla shake."

"How much did she lose last week?"

"Two pounds."

"Not good, Vita, my dear. I will most certainly try."

The mother returned, strawberry terrycloth hugged to her neck and shoulders like a fine, mink stole. Vita couldn't be sure, but she thought she heard her mother giggle.

"And where are we going today?" Vita's mother asked.

"Anywhere you like, darling," Clementine said. "How about the Ritz? Or we can go downtown to Hudson's and eat spinach salad and snack on roasted chestnuts and feed crusts of bread to the pigeons."

Clementine turned to Vita and asked: "Does this young lady have permission to drink a nip of sherry over the meal, if she should like?"

Another giggle.

Vita watched her mother grab Clem's arm and waltz across the yard.

* * *

The round women were born around the same time that Vita started to fade from her mother's memory. This coincidence did not escape Vita's notice. As an artist always imagining, if not actually committing to paper, her self-portrait, Vita tried to remain in tune with what her favorite radio therapist called her "inner goddess." Round women. Earth Mother. Immortal.

Perhaps Vita reached back to her very first image of her mother for inspiration. Perhaps her sculptures were bending over her, thick hair floating forward, stretching down, after she cracked her head on the corner of the family's brick fireplace and experienced her first memory of hot pain. Or it could have even been before then. Before Vita's own memory began. A milky breast pressed between pruned, pink fingers. A soft, warm smell.

Maybe it was all of these things. Maybe the round women popped into a place in Vita's mind where dream and memory and story mix. She gave up her pyramid-scheme cosmetics sales job immediately without regret – honestly, how many self-respecting names for the color red can there be? – and became a potter, a sculptor. A proud maker of these round women.

"What is that you think you're doing?" Vita's mother asked in one of her more lucid moments. Or was it? Either way, it was an unfair question and Vita ignored her. Bills could be managed.

Vita worked in orange clay, a bit muddy and grainy. She collected scraps of cloth, costume jewelry, and other leftovers from her life to complete the round women. She palmed their breasts and thumbed their bellies into balloons. Like children, they had different heights and personalities; they clashed and competed for Vita's attention. But even under glaze and smooth strokes, they all shared impressions from Vita, chunks of her fingerprints.

After her first attempts to sell her round women failed, Vita found places for them in her home: on shelves, the antique highchair, and the round oak table between the olive couch and recliner. She had dozens. "Maybe they belong here," Vita thought. Her mother positioned the round women strategically by frosty front windows and over her bed stand telling them: "Don't move unless I say!" or "Listen for Joshua barking!" or "Pray to the saints for me!"

All single women – Vita and Vita's mother and the round, round clay dolls. All single and unique and strong and real.

* * *

174

Clementine kept Vita's mother out until almost four o'clock. The sun was dusty and sleepy, and yellow clouds were strung across the sky like an amber necklace. She returned with a half-eaten apple on a stick and caramel smudged around her lips.

"Thank you most kindly for the pleasure," Clementine said. He bowed to Vita's mother when he delivered her to her front doorstep.

"You are very welcome," Vita's mother said and then blushed and strolled inside.

Vita waited until she heard her mother's bedroom door click shut.

"Well?" she asked.

"So sorry, Vita dear," Clem said. "Today seemed like one of her good days, but only that half apple. I tried."

"I know you did."

"She's getting too slim," he said.

"I know."

They nodded to each other without saying goodbye.

Within a few minutes, Vita's mother crept out of her room and smiled. Vita asked her: "Why didn't you ask Clem in for dinner?"

"This was only our first date, Pennsylvania," Vita's mother said. "A girl doesn't want to be too forward."

Vita's mother sat at the table and began reading the newspaper from back to front. She left tiny, gray fingerprints on the corner of each page.

"What's for breakfast, Rhode Island?"

Vita put a slice of bread in the toaster and made some coffee.

REV. ROBERT A. YOUNG (1893-1977)
Gary Young

> *"Verily I say unto you, whosoever*
> *shall not receive the kingdom of God*
> *as a little child, he shall not enter therein."*
> Mark 10:15

Ill, shaken and hollowed out, he remained
the best of what he had been, the mad preacher
delivering sermons to the wall, entreating
the curtains to be wary of their pride.

This man once held me
spellbound from the pulpit, the only preacher
I could ever sit still for.
If age stole his vigor and withered him
he avenged himself with good deeds
and better. If the world was lost, spirit
was everywhere waiting to bless and be blessed.

I still see him standing in the fog
of his failed senses, hands gesturing
to a phantom couple who have come
to be married by Dr. Young, here
in the corner of his bedroom.
Do you take this woman, he asks,
Do you take this man? And I hear them
answer each in turn, *I do, I do, I do.*

THE OLD MAN'S LOVE
J. J. Steinfeld

Although he had been in the hospital for three weeks and spoke infrequently – and then usually about long-past days and not to anyone in the room – the old man had no shortage of visitors. At ninety, he was the oldest living member of a large, and, as family members liked to repeat, closely-knit family. During visiting hours the old man was never alone, as if there was a mandatory bedside vigil being conducted.

"Helen, my dearest Helen, the way you make love...you make me forget everything...you make me scream with desire," the old man said, and the nearby woman, who was one of his eighteen grandchildren, hurriedly ushered her young son out of the room.

"Don't take it so seriously," the woman's husband called after her, but she was already out in the hallway.

He wanted to hear more, but the old man had fallen silent, even though his lips continued to move and his eyes indicated that his mind was journeying elsewhere.

At that moment, in the confinement of his hospital bed, the old man loved Helen as much as he had loved her over seventy years ago, more, if that were possible. He hadn't seen Helen once in all that time, not once.

* * *

The youngest and oldest of the old man's eight children – a woman of forty-nine, who was divorced and had three teenage children – and a man of sixty-three – who was a lifelong bachelor – stood in the hospital room without speaking. The woman began to cry and said that if their mother were still alive, things would be better for the stricken old man on the bed. As she did during each visit, the woman told the story of how their beloved parents had been childhood sweethearts, engaged at seventeen, and of their long, romantic, nine-year engagement.

"Cold feet... Dad probably had more than a couple of bouts of cold feet," the sixty-three-year-old bachelor said. Their father had been a widower for nearly twenty years now.

The old man scratched at the sheets near his neck, attempting to lower them, and started to call out the name "Helen." His voice was not strong, but there was no absence of yearning or passion in his words.

"Who in the world is Helen?" the old man's daughter asked.

"I don't have a clue," the old man's son replied.

"He doesn't say our mother's name," the daughter said, turning with an expression of scorn towards her father.

"He doesn't know what he's saying, Christ Almighty," the man defended his bedridden father.

"It's foul the way his tongue hangs out of his mouth," the old man's daughter said, and she became angry with herself for wishing her father dead.

* * *

The old man could feel his lips against the collar of Helen's bright-green blouse. He chewed and chewed on the collar, a nervous young man of nineteen, made more nervous by the young woman's boldness. In the car, with its smell of newness, Helen touched him where his fiancée wouldn't even look.

Then against their better judgment, they undressed, left the car, and began to make love on the moist grass next to the car; it was a new automobile that she had taken from a neighbor's yard without his permission.

Helen was a fearless freethinker, and he loved those qualities, loved them even as they frightened him. Each time he made love with her was different, more frightening, yet harder to resist than the previous time.

Helen told him to think of her when he made love to his new wife, and he replied (both in passion and with the knowledge of the futility of his declaration) that he loved only her and wanted to live with her.

* * *

The old man would sometimes move a single hand in the air, as if attempting to capture or retrieve something, a butterfly or a thought, or perhaps a regret.

A dark-haired doctor, who several of the women in the family thought was handsome, prescribed a stronger dosage of medication, so the old man's stay in the hospital would be more restful, less troubled.

A twenty-one-year-old grandson, who had musical ability that was often compared to his grandfather's (but who had exhibited little ambition so far), questioned the handsome doctor's decision to subdue the little movement his grandfather showed.

The doctor lowered the old man's hand to his chest and said, "Do you want him to talk about having sex with Helen all the time and hurt himself when he's so helplessly disoriented?"

The grandson argued that his grandfather's sex talk was not frequent, and so far as he saw, it didn't threaten the morals of the hospital staff. The doctor merely smiled and told the young man to leave medical matters in his hands.

Still, despite the stronger dosage of medication, the old man continued to talk about Helen, and to Helen, though less frequently and in an even softer voice. When his hand went into the air, it was not as high and for not as long.

Amid the voices of a family squabble he did not comprehend, the old man clearly saw in his mind his parents standing with him on the pier, urging him to board the ship for France; all the arrangements had been made. He told his parents he didn't want to study music in Paris. He was destined to become a great musician, his father argued, and his mother pleaded with her nineteen-year-old son to be reasonable and not jeopardize his future.

"Where is Helen?" he shouted at his parents so loud that some of the passengers already on the ocean liner looked down towards the pier for the source of the commotion.

"Forget about that whore," his father told him.

The son hit his father in the face, then quickly and without apology boarded the ship for France and the continuation of his musical training. He had begun playing the violin when he was barely six and had progressed steadily, outgrowing three teachers. In Paris, he would have world-caliber guidance and instruction; it was the chance of a lifetime. For much of the trip across the Atlantic, he looked at the water and searched for Helen, even if only in his imagination. Occasionally a wind-churned wave appeared to be shaped like a soft bed where he could join his love. The only time the brilliant young musician did not feel doomed was when he took out the photographs of his true love, photographs of her without clothing that she had posed especially for him. How Helen had laughed and kissed him when she gave him the photographs. Embarrassed, shaking his head in both admiration and disbelief, he swore that he would never part with those forbidden love offerings.

* * *

The youngest great-grandchild, a curly-haired boy of three, was brought into the hospital room to see his only living great-grandparent, the famous violinist who had performed (according to family legend) in over fifty countries and before several heads of state and numerous members of royalty. In reality, it had been only fourteen countries – for he was a reluctant traveler throughout his life – but Edward VIII, before his abdication, had indeed commented after a concert in England that he had played with celestial inspiration. One of the old man's violins, the oldest and most valuable in his large collection, was going to this child, a decision made on the day the boy was born. The old man's will had been revised many times over the years, and it was now clear as to who would be getting each of his magnificent violins, along with his money and the dark, heavy furniture in his large apartment. The precious photographs hidden away in a safe-deposit box, according to the Will, were to be cremated with him and the ashes thrown into the Atlantic Ocean, preferably from the deck of a ship sailing for France.

* * *

Long after visiting hours were over, a thick-eyebrowed, narrow-lipped doctor, who was about to finish his shift, called one of his colleagues into the room where they listened to the old man talk about making love.

180

"There's a nurse in pediatrics named Helen, but you wouldn't want to screw her if your life depended on it," the narrow-lipped doctor said as he rubbed his thick eyebrows.

"I never thought you were fussy," his colleague teased.

"Quiet," the first doctor ordered, playfully pushing his colleague closer to the old man's bed, "you'll ruin my spotless reputation."

"It's like he's describing his wedding night."

"Do you realize he's older than both of us put together?"

"The poor bastard lived alone until last month, do you believe it? Then he fell off a chair."

"Fell off trying to get at an old violin of his up on a high shelf, I heard."

The old man became silent and the two doctors left the room, starting another conversation about the nurses in pediatrics.

* * *

"He was a beautiful, beautiful man. As good-looking as Rudolph Valentino, my mother used to say. I have pictures of my father as a young man. Seventy-year-old stuff, collector's items," the old man's fifty-three-year-old daughter told her companion, a man both much shorter and considerably younger than she. This woman had scandalized the family on other occasions, but not as much as this time, with her twenty-seven-year-old lover.

"No, they couldn't be that old," the man said, as if anything before he was born had become dust long ago.

"Sure, my mother gave them to me when I started getting serious about painting."

"You ever paint him?"

"In my first show I had a wonderful oil painting of a beautiful young man playing the violin in front of the Eiffel Tower. I got $275 for it – a fortune back then."

"You used to sell work that cheap?"

"Listen, I paid a month's rent and bought my first husband a new suit with that money."

"You told me that was your only show without nudes."

"I had done plenty of nudes, but I was afraid to show them in those days."

"Not anymore," the man said, and he tried to fondle the woman's breasts.

"Remember where we are," she scolded him sharply.

181

"Let's go home and I'll pose naked for you."
"I want to keep my father company."
"He doesn't know you're here."
"He's still my father."
"You think he'll talk dirty again today?"

* * *

It wasn't until the old man had been in the hospital a month that someone thought of bringing in one of his violins. All the violins were valuable, and there was some disagreement among family members as to the wisdom of leaving a valuable instrument in a hospital room with a man who didn't know where he was or, for that matter, who he was.

Finally, a nineteen-year-old granddaughter took the key from her mother's coat pocket, went to the old man's apartment, removed a violin – not knowing if it was the oldest or most valuable – and brought it to the hospital room. Her mother and a dozen other relatives had warned her against doing this, but the young woman took the responsibility upon herself. The old man hadn't played publicly – not even for the family – in twenty years, but his reputation was intact. Even the younger family members, who had never heard him perform live, often heard the recordings from earlier years that had won him much acclaim when they were played at family gatherings. As he got older, before the hospital, you could stand outside his apartment door and hear him playing the violin at all hours, but he would stop whenever someone arrived and then deny that he had been playing.

The independent-minded granddaughter held the violin in front of the old man, but he didn't seem to respond to her presence, only uttering a few words about Helen with his eyes closed.

The young woman put the violin and its case on the small table next to the old man's bed and threatened to make miserable the life of any family member who even suggested that the exquisite instrument shouldn't be left there.

After that she started to bring a sketchpad to the hospital room to draw the old man and his violin. Her mother – a very successful artist who had recently started

182

living with a man only eight years older than her daughter – wanted her talented, strong-willed daughter to return to art college, but the young woman said she was going to spend the next year or two in Europe.

Sometimes as the young artist sketched, her grandfather whispered erotic stories about Helen. On occasion, the old man uttered tiny sobs, as he wondered out loud if Helen had become pregnant and what had become of their child.

* * *

On the old man's ninety-first birthday, ten family members crowded into the hospital room – a concession the hospital administration had made after much arguing with the family. There were twice that many in the hallway and down in the lobby waiting to pay their respects to the old man, when he reached a hand towards the violin on the small table next to his bed. The young artist put down her sketchpad and carefully handed her grandfather his violin. Everyone in the room stared at the old man, waiting, anticipating a concert as great as those in the recordings. He did not play the violin, but instead he held the instrument to his chest, as if it were someone he loved dearly, very dearly.

* * *

A week after his ninety-first birthday, the decision was made at a family meeting to move the old man to a nursing home. Some members of the family dared to say, "to die," but others thought that he would recover and live to be a hundred.

One son, as though giving an impassioned after-dinner speech, claimed that through his recordings their father was immortal and that his frail old body was inconsequential. An argument ensued over the nature and value of immortality.

After still another discussion about the transfer to a nursing home had ended and only two of the old man's relatives remained in the hospital room, he called out Helen's name, desperately wailing for her companionship.

"He was never good to your mother," the husband of the old man's second oldest daughter said. They were a couple whose marriage was held together only by deception and inertia. They always stumbled into one dispute or another when they visited the old man.

"You don't know shit," the woman said defiantly to her husband.

"He's about to croak and all he talks about is sex with other women!" the man said in angry rebuttal.

"Only Helen."

"Your mother's name was Edna."

"So what?"

"So your father's an adulterous old fool, in a manner of speaking, right up to the last friggin' second, that's what."

* * *

The old man turned onto his side, an effort that took all his strength and determination. He looked deep into the ocean water and called out Helen's name with all the longing in his heart. In the end, he refused to board the ship for France and was reunited at last with his beloved Helen. The old man died peacefully, but not alone. At the end, his mind went through seventy orderly years of life with Helen – through the courtship, the wedding, the loving marriage, the rearing of children, the growing old together without relinquishing any important dreams. They went through seventy years of life together with a kindness only a compassionate God could grant.

A MARRIAGE
Carol Nolde

They'd been married sixty years when he noticed
she'd gaze distracted, wondering
if she'd put baking powder in the blueberry pancakes.
Then she forgot names, faces,
then how to button her dress
so he took care of her
bathed and dressed her
and every Sunday bundled her into their old Chevy.
They crept along backroads that crisscrossed the
farmlands,
Aunt Rose's eyes barely above the window frame.
The day they caught me raking leaves from the ditch,
Uncle Willy rolled the window down.
We talked and Aunt Rose smiled and nodded
her wrinkled hand a claw on the door
her bright eyes blank behind glasses.
I thought of their farmhouse cradled in the fold of hills
that were their hayfields and pastures,
the barn full of cattle, the house full of children.
Now the barn long empty
the girls in New Jersey, Pennsylvania, Alaska.

They said Uncle Willy nursed Rose for weeks that winter
sat by the bed listening for her breath
and when he knew the end was near,
he climbed into the hollow in the bed beside her
and held her in his arms.

LIFE WITH IRMA
Jessica Bryan

My mother made bonsai trees. Trimming the roots and curving the branches, she created her own vision of beauty. She also owned ninety-seven cactus plants. Summer mornings I carried them out to the yard for sun, and in the evening I brought them in. One winter we made Christmas corsages and I stood on a street corner near the bus stop with a board around my neck displaying them for sale. If I asked for a dress I'd seen in a store window, she would draw a picture of it and produce an identical copy with her sewing machine.

She could read a book, knit a pair of argyle socks for my father, listen to the radio, and analyze a television program plot all at the same time, never losing track of any of it. When I was eleven, she complained she was bored because she had read all the books in the neighborhood library. She was a great cook and baked her own bread. The three of us lived on $10 a week.

Irma's hair was always very curly. She was so proud of it that at the end, just before she gave up talking completely, her curly hair was the only subject she'd discuss. Being only 4'10" tall was her biggest regret, and according to her, it ruined her life by rendering her ineffectual in a world of larger, more aggressive people.

Later, when I was a teenager, she went to work in the candy department at Woolworth's where she got fat from eating candy, until I was finally able to persuade her to get a better job at a florist where they sold original Salvador Dali vases. She read Ayn Rand – who believed the concept of God is morally evil as it implies man's inferiority – and attempted, without success, to indoctrinate me.

When I was fifteen years old, Irma made me swear if she ever got seriously sick I would refrain from calling a doctor to perform heroic procedures, but would let her die a natural death. She kept a bottle of Phenobarbital hidden in her dresser drawer for twenty years, telling me it was her ticket out of this world when she got old.

Together we devoured Ray Bradbury's books and *The Twilight Zone*. When I was seventeen, and we were living in Philadelphia, Irma owned the best jazz record collection north of Olney Avenue. My friends would come over to listen to her records and drink gin. I disliked jazz. I considered myself a beatnik and only listened to folk music – except on Mother's Day in 1967 when I took her to hear Frank Zappa and the Mothers of Invention.

When I turned on to marijuana, so did Irma. She told me it was good for her heart. So proud that my mom was "hip," I mailed her pot from wherever I traveled, until I was twenty-four when I began searching for a more permanent, less artificial means of achieving inner satisfaction.

Irma and I were friends until I became a teenager and our relationship began to crumble under the weight of my tempestuous sexuality and her disgust with anything sexual. When I was eighteen, I moved out of the house and continued to move farther and farther from her until she was sixty-five years old, and I returned to visit her in Philadelphia. Having been divorced from my father several years earlier, she was no longer working and lived alone in an apartment above the flower shop.

Street Stories

North Philly, Irma's apartment on North Broad Street, and Irma are showing signs of decay. Outside, gangs roam the once peaceful neighborhood and garbage is piled in the gutters. Inside, the wallpaper has turned yellow and is peeling off the ceiling in the dining room. It hangs there, threatening the table where we sit eating breakfast – ten bottles of vitamin pills, a pile of newspapers, two pairs of eyeglasses, and a box of chocolate-covered cherries separating us.

"Just the other day I went to Penn Fruit to buy cheesecake, but they didn't have the kind I like," she said.

"What did you do?"

"I was standing in the parking lot when I met this nice man."

"Did you talk to him?" I ask, afraid of the answer she might give.

"Oh yes, he was such a nice man. He drove me in his car to another store to buy cheesecake and then he took me home." She seemed quite pleased with the cake and exhilarated from her meeting with a stranger.

Something is wrong, but I don't understand what it is. I consider telling George, my brother who lives in Tennessee, that his mother has been picking up strange men in parking lots and I decide against it.

Irma's sense of aesthetics has quite obviously changed. She proudly shows me two drawers full of cheap plastic jewelry, and for the duration of my visit she refuses to wear anything except dingy gray pants and matching shirt, although her closet is filled with brightly-colored things. She appears apathetic and listless. The kitchen is littered with dirty dishes, copies of the *National Enquirer*, and magazines about UFOs landing in Arizona. She tells me her greatest wish is to live long enough to see aliens from outer space visit America. Her books sit unread on the shelves and the stereo is broken.

Irma has two thousand dollars hidden in the sofa – money earned from taking care of the ninety-year-old woman who lives downstairs. Irma feeds her a bowl of soup at noon and neither of them sees or talks with anyone else all day.

She tells me another street story:

"Oh, the most horrible thing happened last week."

"What was it?"

"You know, I wanted to sell my refrigerator. Well, one day I met a man downstairs and we were talking about the refrigerator. He wanted to see it, but when he came upstairs he tried to kiss me. It was just awful! He put his smelly ol' tongue down my throat. What should I do Jessie?"

Without answering, I grab the phone and call my brother and demand he do something immediately. I tell him his mother has been picking up men on the street and insist we move her to Tennessee where he can protect her. It seems like the obvious solution, since he's been living in the same town for fifteen years and I move frequently. Poor George, he was the child of Irma's first marriage, but when she divorced his father and married my father, George and her new husband didn't get along. To eliminate the conflict, Irma sent him to live with her mother when he was seven, and he has never forgiven her. Now I'm asking him to help her, and although he'd rather ignore us both, he finally agrees she can come to Tennessee. George signs her up for low income housing for the elderly and we begin waiting for her turn to move in. Fortunately, an apartment becomes available after only three months, at which time George and I rendezvous at her apartment in Philadelphia.

* * *

Irma is excited about moving. She's ready to leave all her junk behind, including Timmy, her paranoid cat, who refuses to come out from behind the sofa. It's a purge, as she scrutinizes each item carefully and then tells us to pack it in the U-Haul or throw it out. She tells us she can't read anymore and insists on giving her books away, but then she cries when they are carried out the door. George throws away her bottle of Phenobarbital when she's not looking.

When she waves goodbye to me from the cab of the U-Haul, I feel relieved, because I know George will take care of her. She'll stay with him and his family for a few weeks and then move into her new apartment.

* * *

My feeling of relief doesn't last long. George calls me a few days later from Tennessee in desperation, his normally steady voice shaking with frustration. Irma is driving him and his family crazy.

"SHE PUT ALL THE DIRTY SHEETS IN THE OVEN," he screams. "WHY CAN'T MY MOTHER BE NORMAL LIKE EVERYONE ELSE'S?"

He's convinced she's losing her mind because she took Dexedrine for ten years to lose weight and because she was depressed.

I think it's hysterically funny that she put the sheets in the oven, but how can I tell him? He's lost his sense of humor, because the perfect picture he has of his life is crumbling. She's only trying to help with the housework, but George has no patience with her seemingly irrational behavior. Fortunately, she moves into her new apartment after spending only two weeks with him and his family.

Call For Help

While Irma was getting settled in her new apartment in Tennessee, I was traveling with Swami Muktananda, affectionately known as "Baba." He was a meditation teacher who had the ability to awaken the spiritual potential in others. Revered in his own country for his spiritual attainment and the universality of his teachings, he taught thousands of people all over the world to meditate. I studied with him because I wanted to experience peace.

Things appeared to be going smoothly for Irma, until about a year later when I received a phone call: "I'm so miserable; I want to kill myself; I drank a bottle of dish detergent, but it only made me throw up."

Urging her to calm down, I promise to come to Tennessee and take her to New York with me. Swami Muktananda is just about to leave Florida and spend another summer at his meditation center in South Fallsburg. I'm hoping that once we get there, he'll help me straighten things out.

Before leaving Florida, I tell him about my mother's condition, and he replies, "Tell her to be happy, tell her to live." He agrees she should come to New York and shortly thereafter I leave for Tennessee to pick her up.

Nothing could have prepared me for the shock of seeing Irma again. She's lost about thirty pounds and there's no food in the apartment. When I take her shopping, all she's interested in is candy, celery, and English muffins. She is unable to hold a coherent conversation and repeats the same questions over and over, until I'm totally exasperated from giving the same answers. Since I haven't had any experience with older people, I don't realize she's suffering from an illness. I merely assume the strange behavior of her youth has gotten stranger with her advancing age.

When I change the sheets on her bed, I get so angry with my brother I start crying. The sheets appear to have been on the mattress the whole year she's been living in Tennessee, and there is half an inch of dead, dry skin between them at the foot of the bed. I carry the sheets with two fingers of one hand, and holding my nose with the other, cram them down the garbage disposal in the hallway.

When I question George, he says, "I come and see her every week and take her shopping." His bewilderment is genuine, but it doesn't explain what went wrong here. Although this is a beautiful, modern housing project for the elderly with a recreation hall, counselors and other social services for the residents, Irma has apparently had little contact with anyone. Evidently, her insecurity has deepened in her old age, and she's been sitting in her new apartment since she moved in, eating little, watching TV, and becoming more and more depressed and disconnected from reality. Even if someone had reached out to her, she must have been unable to respond.

When I take her down to the lobby and attempt three-way conversation with another old lady, she gives us the snub, probably because we're Yankees.

We Take a Vacation

Everything I own is crammed into the old Dodge, including Bobo, my fourteen-year-old cat. There's just barely room for Irma and her suitcase, but off we go, headed for New York.

Irma loves being on the road and spends carefree hours enjoying the scenery and eating in restaurants. When she gets bored, she fiddles with the radio knobs, or I give her my purse to play with. She throws the contents about the car and writes nonsense syllables on the checks in my checkbook.

The first night we stay in a hotel where she keeps getting up to search for the bathroom and the second we visit a meditation center, which is in a private home in Virginia. The family who lives there agrees to put us up for the night.

While helping with the dishes after dinner, I hear a loud crash, and when I run into the living room, I see Irma has slipped and fallen down a whole flight of stairs and landed on her back. Fortunately, she suffers no fractures, only bruises that spread ominously over her left arm and leg during the next three weeks. I'm suddenly terrified, as I begin to realize that I've assumed responsibility for another

191

human being, one who obviously needs a great deal of supervision.

* * *

When we arrive in South Fallsburg, we move into a one-room bungalow near the meditation center. It's a sunny, cheerful little place with twin beds, table and chairs, and wooden paneling all around. It's spotlessly clean. The Italian family who lives on the property and rents out the bungalow is quite friendly and they even offer to let us use their swimming pool. There are lawn chairs out front under the tall pine trees and the air is fresh and clean.

Here in New York, I'm confronted with the reality of living with my mother again, after fourteen years on my own. Sometimes she's the person I've always known, but then again, she is also like a child – an unpredictable child. Who I am required to be changes from moment to moment and it's confusing. Often she accuses me of stealing her money, or bemoans the fact she has no money, so I give her a little purse with several dollars in it. I always tell her, "Don't worry Irma; we have lots of money in the bank."

We become involved in small intimacies, like my giving her a bath, fixing her hair, and cutting her toenails. It's like playing house with a real live doll. After I have given her a bath, I put her clothes on the bed – panties, bra, stockings, shirt, and pants – and ask her to get dressed while I take a shower. When I come out of the bathroom, invariably she has everything on, except that the bra and panties are on top of the shirt and pants, or in some other confused order. I can't help laughing at her, but when she realizes how funny she looks, she laughs too.

After several months, I run out of money and go to work part-time as a camp counselor. Arriving home from work the first day, I encounter a disaster. Imagine letting a two-year-old alone in the house for five hours to play freely. She has carefully washed all the dishes and put them in the refrigerator to dry. In an attempt to feed Bobo, she has put his cat food in the kitty litter box. The contents of her suitcase are strewn about the room.

What really upsets me is she's put her wig and a box of corn flakes on the "puja." A puja is an altar where one keeps things of religious significance, like pictures of saints, flowers, or other offerings to God – the Hindu version of an altar. It's the holy corner of the room, and our holy corner has been desecrated by cornflakes!

Looking wild about the eyes, Irma sits calmly in the front yard. After complaining about the mess for a few minutes, I realize she has no idea whatsoever why I'm upset.

Late in the evening, after she has gone to sleep or early in the morning before she wakes, I sit for meditation. Caressed by the moonlight streaming in through the window, I turn inside to that still, quiet, joyful center within myself where there is no Irma, there is no Jessie, and there is no outside world with its attendant grief and problems – that place inside where there is only strength, peace, and renewal.

Irma Meets Swami Muktananda

We go to the meditation center often to attend the programs. One day when we arrive, I have a difficult time convincing Irma to part with her shoes and leave them in the shoe room. She's quite attached to her shoes; they're those little black Chinese slippers and she just loves them. After lengthy negotiations, we sit in the back of the meditation hall. Now, all the mothers and children also sit in the back of the hall, and Irma has become fascinated with children. All through the program she amuses herself – and annoys me and everyone else – saying, "Oh Jessie, look at the beautiful baby," and grabbing for every kid that walks or crawls by. She's so happy; I don't want to tell her to be quiet.

After Baba's talk and group chanting, it's time for "darshan," which means "to greet." During darshan, people go up in a line three or four across down the center aisle to greet Baba. Each person brings a gift, a piece of fruit, or a flower. Baba is wrapped in a blaze of glorious orange, shining like the sun, as he gently hits each person on the head with his wand of peacock feathers. He talks to some and ignores others. Some also receive gifts or the answer to a question.

Irma and I take our place in the darshan line. Then, when the moment arrives and we are standing before him, simultaneously two things happen. He looks at her directly and hits her with the feathers to get her attention, but she is looking elsewhere. She is looking down at her feet and exclaiming, "WHERE ARE MY SHOES?" Everyone laughs as Baba bops her again and asks playfully in English, "HOW ARE YOU?" Irma continues to examine her socks, as we exit amidst the peals of laughter.

Because she doesn't expect or understand his attention – the attention everyone in the room is hoping for – she gets it tenfold.

Irma Changes Her Name

One day Irma announces she wants a new name. Someone must have told her Swami Muktananda gives people spiritual names. She tells me her name "Irma" is "too sharp." I tell her she has to ask him for the name herself.

As we wait our turn in the darshan line, I explain how to ask for a name and somehow she manages to do it. Baba gives her a little white card with her new name printed on it: "Chandra," the Hindi word for the moon. It's the perfect name because Irma loves the moon and spends hours outside gazing at it when it's full.

She loves her new name and insists everyone use it. The only problem is she can't remember the name. At least fifty times a day she asks me, "What's my new name?"

"Chandra," I reply.

"Oh, Sandra."

"NO! CHANDRA!"

Finally I get tired of answering and start calling her Sandra, until the day arrives when she forgets she ever had a new name.

Billie

Billie hates to wear shoes and he has the youngest looking feet I've ever seen on an old man. They are always filthy. In the winter he wears socks, but shoes are only for dress-up trips to town on check-cashing day and other special occasions. Billie's hair is completely white and his eyes are a brilliant blue, like the summer sky in the Catskills.

194

He's an old salt. By that I mean he was a sailor years ago, but to hear him talk, it was only yesterday, and all the years in between don't exist. He relishes his memories of wild nights in hotels and bars with his buddies and "indecent" women. Try as I might, I can never convince him to give me the spicy details. Perhaps there are none and he's only making it up.

Billie is proud, independent, fiery, and forceful. He almost knocks me over with his opinions and enthusiasm. He's in his seventies, but he seems seventeen. He makes mysteriously whispered phone calls and drops hints regarding passionate younger women he expects to meet for secret rendezvous.

His left arm is very expensive. It cost the State of New York Ninety-Five Thousand Dollars (and Billie six months in the hospital) to keep it attached to his body after he was hit on the road by a truck ten years ago. It hangs there lifelessly – periodically swollen and purple – nursed, bandaged, and loved. Every winter the doctor tries to convince Billie to have it surgically removed, but he won't hear of it. By God, he'll be a whole man till he dies. I understand why all his life he's been called "Tiger."

Although Billie seems quite strong, his health is tenuous. He has a bad heart and he uses it to his advantage. When he gets angry, or people don't do what he wants them to do, he goes to the hospital. It's his entertainment, his vacation from responsibility. The nurses fuss over him and someone else does the cooking. I envy him. When anything goes wrong, Billie just checks into the hospital for some tender, loving care.

Billie's closets are filled with expensive clothing: suits, shirts, socks, coats, and drawers of underwear, but still he insists on wearing rags. I think he'd really rather go naked. Like a lot of old-timers who remember the Great Depression, Billie hoards things. He has something for every occasion and is prepared for any emergency. There is one thousand dollars worth of food stashed in the cupboard and money buried in the front yard. Billie's small, two-room bungalow in the Catskills is bursting at the seams!

Because he only has one useful arm, the place is always a mess, and although he is constantly cleaning, it never gets clean. I step carefully over dog hairs on the floor and avoid the congealed grease in the sink, living in terror of the day my brother might come for a visit and see this mess. When Billie knows I'm coming to town, he throws out the worst of the dirty dishes and ferrets new ones from the closet in my honor.

Irma and I strike an uneasy truce with Billie's beloved dogs, Bobo and Little Boy, who bark most of the night and fight over the scraps of food he throws on the floor for them. Temperamental creatures, they adore him, but barely hide their distain for Irma and me.

Irma and Billie Fall in Love

Since Irma can't be left alone during the day, I ask Billie who lives just down the road, if he will watch her while I'm at work. He's overjoyed at the prospect of having company and readily agrees. After about a week, much to my surprise, Irma and Billie fall in love.

One day stands out vividly in my memory. It's a beautiful summer day in the mountains. Irma and I are sitting out in the yard dozing in the sun, when I see Billie coming down the road. He looks fantastic. He's wearing newly-shined white buck shoes, pressed slacks, and a beautiful blue shirt, the same shade of blue as his eyes. His hair is neatly combed, and judging by the little cuts all over his face and the pervasive odor of cologne, he has just shaved.

Billie has come courting Irma! He's brought her flowers and we all sit together in the yard. They're nervous like two teenagers. After he leaves, all she can say is, "His eyes are so blue. He's such a nice man." She asks me about twenty times "What happened to his arm, poor thing?"

Before long, they start talking about getting married, and I begin to get nervous. Then one day they announce they are getting married and insist I take them for a marriage license. I have serious doubts about Irma's ability to understand the marriage ceremony, but before we can go to City Hall, Billie gets cold feet and calls off the wedding. Then suddenly he changes his mind again and wants to go through with it. I tell them they have to get blood tests for syphilis (which is totally ridiculous since they aren't likely to be having children.) But they are determined to get married, so off to the doctor we go. The doctor is Chinese and seems to think we're all crazy.

Then Irma gets cold feet, and so it goes back and forth. I'm really hoping their relationship will work out. They'd be good company for each other in their old age. Finally they compromise and decide to live together and try it out, like the younger generation does.

Irma moves in with Billie and things are going along fine for a few weeks, until one morning I see her running down the road towards my bungalow. "I'm so angry with that man! He's a bum! What a jerk! I hate that man!" she states emphatically.

When she calms down I question her carefully, "Just what happened?"

She replies with great disgust, "THAT MAN took out his you-know-what and tried to get me to touch it! I'm NEVER going back there again!"

I'm astonished. It never occurred to me Billie would try to have sex with her. He only has one good arm and a bad heart – who would suspect him of trying to fool around?

I go over to his bungalow and attempt to straighten things out. I tell him, "Irma has never liked sex; she complained about it for years. She won't change her mind."

Billie is extremely agitated. "What do you expect me to do, hang it out the window?" he demands. After lengthy negotiations, I go home and discuss the situation with her. It's a standoff; she refuses to go anywhere near him.

Two days later I hear Billie's in the hospital. I'm certain he's not sick, just upset Irma rejected his amorous advances. I explain to her carefully that Billie is having heart trouble and he's in the hospital. She agrees to go with me to visit him, and on the way to the hospital we stop and pick orange tiger lilies by the side of the road. I try to prepare her for the visit by saying, "When we get to the hospital, you go in the room first and hand him the flowers." She nods in agreement, but I'm not certain she really understands.

When we arrive at the door to his hospital room – Irma with flowers in hand – and she sees him lying there in bed, she screams, "Oh Billie, you poor thing, I LOVE YOU, I LOVE YOU," and proceeds to throw herself and the flowers on top of him right then and there.

That seals it. Irma and Billie are a number. She moves back into his bungalow for better or worse. Fortunately, they don't bring up the subject of marriage licenses again. Billie doesn't discuss the topic of sex either, and I can only assume he's resigned himself to a sexless romance with Irma.

Billie tells me with tears in his eyes, "No one has ever brought me flowers before in my whole life."

Billie's Relationship with Swami Muktananda

Billie proudly informs me, "Oh yes! Me and THE BABA are good friends."

"How's that?"

"I visit him all the time and we talk," he replies, looking pleased with his audacity.

"What do you talk about?"

"I showed him the rose bushes I planted by his house when it used to be Jack's house. I helped Jack build that house, you know."

"Is that all you talk about?"

"We talk about dogs!" he exclaims, as if there is no other subject worth discussing.

* * *

About once a week, Billie decides to go to the meditation center with us. He starts preparing for the five o'clock program around two o'clock. First, he shaves clumsily, that takes almost an hour. Then he gets dressed in his best suit and fancy white shoes. He is ready to leave at least an hour before we are and sits impatiently in the front yard waiting to go. With his hair all slicked back, he looks like a small boy waiting for someone to take him to first grade.

When Irma and I are dressed, we leave for the program. I already know the scenario that will follow. First we go into the dining room where he fusses over the flowers for sale. Finally, choosing the three most beautiful roses to give Baba, he magnanimously pays for them. Then, after leaving our shoes in the shoe room, we go into the meditation hall where he sits stiffly in his chair.

After about five minutes – before the program has even started – Billie starts to wiggle in his chair and sweat

198

profusely. He hands me the roses and apologizes, saying, "I can't take it, the air-conditioning bothers my heart," as he runs out of the hall.

Winter Stories

Billie has become the perpetual feeder. In his zealousness to entertain Irma, he feeds her constantly. They get up for breakfast at two a.m., five a.m., and eight a.m. In the long dark of the New York winter nights we go from one feeding to the next. I'm losing sleep and Irma's getting fatter and fatter. Actually, she's become a little butterball, but Billie thinks she's cute. When she approaches size sixteen and her clothes no longer fit, I begin to oppose him.

Then it's one argument after another – arguments over one more banana, one more slice of bread. I insist she go on a diet, but Billie feeds her pie to gain her favor when I'm not looking. Finally I realize I've lost the battle and surrender. She won't die any sooner from getting fat.

* * *

Irma roams the small bedroom in Billie's bungalow asking urgently, "Where's my mother? She never comes to see me anymore."

What can I say? That her mother died twenty years ago? I say it, and she begins to weep. She can't comprehend twenty years or even twenty minutes. She lives in the moment and this moment, for her, her mother has just died.

Damn! Why didn't I just lie and tell her, "Your mother's coming tomorrow." By the next day she would have forgotten and tonight she would have been satisfied.

I question whether I should conform to her reality, or impose my reality on her?

* * *

Late into the evening Irma and I listen to the radio and dance together in the small space left free from Billie's excess belongings. It's Aretha Franklin, and we shake our hips and laugh. Music is one way we still connect, now that it's getting harder and harder to have a conversation.

* * *

Shortly after I return home from my Christmas visit, I dream Irma is in danger and needs help. The next morning I call her and ask, "How are you? Is everything all right?"

Her voice sounds weak as she replies, "Oh, I guess so, but it's cold in here and I can't get the stove to work. I'm hungry and the can opener is broken."

"Where's Billie?"

"Oh, I haven't seen that man for a long time."

Realizing something is indeed seriously wrong, I hang up and call a neighbor who goes over to check. Sure enough, Irma is home alone and the heat is turned off. I make several more calls and find Billie in the hospital in Monticello. When I ask him what happened, he tells me he had heart pains, but before he went to the hospital, he arranged for Irma to stay with his friend, Jack, who lives in Hurleyville.

As the story unfolds further, it appears Irma was unhappy at Jack's. She missed Billie and decided to go home. The local police picked her up on the road, and recognizing her as the eccentric lady who lived with Billie, they brought her to the bungalow, not realizing Billie wasn't there to take care of her.

Billie's doctor solves the problem with an unusual solution. In order to keep them together – and Irma under his watchful eye – he signs her into the hospital too. He writes on the chart, "Admit for check-up." Then he assigns her the bed next to Billie and they have a cozy winter vacation in the hospital together!

Irma and Billie Go to The Bank

Billie takes care of Irma's money and the local bank has been directed to allow him to cash her Social Security checks. In addition, he has a written statement explaining the situation that he can show to anyone who questions his authority over her or her business.

One rainy winter day, Irma and Billie go to the bank to cash her check. On the way she slips and falls in a puddle, getting her pants wet. When they arrive at the bank, the teller asks her, "How did you get your pants wet?"

Irma replies, "How do you think?" and proceeds to pull down her pants right there in the bank lobby.

Billie roars with laughter. He thinks this is the funniest thing he's ever seen. The bank employees are not impressed, however, they're embarrassed.

One of the bank officers comes over and asks Irma, indicating Billie, "Are you giving him all your money?"

"Of course, what else do you expect me to do with it?"

The official points to Billie again and asks her, "Do you know that man?"

"Why I've never seen him before in my life," she answers.

Thinking Billie is stealing her money, the bank officer demands, "Why are you trying to cash her check?" Billie shows him the letter from me and when he's told that's not good enough he really loses his temper and begins to yell at the bank officer: "I'm a local boy. You call the Chief of Police; he's a friend of mine. This woman lives at my bungalow colony and I'm her landlord. She pays her rent to me and I take care of all her business."

When the bank official hears Billie is the owner of a bungalow colony (which isn't true) he relents and cashes her check!

Irma Goes To Texas

In the spring I receive a call from Billie: "Irma keeps running away from home. As soon as I lay down for a nap, she's out the door and down the road as fast as her little feet can carry her," he complains. "Locking the door don't help, Jessie. I even tried nailing it shut, but she finds the hammer and gets it open."

He puts Irma on the phone and I threaten various punishments (including banishment to a nursing home) if she doesn't stop trying to run away, but she doesn't react or seem to understand what I'm talking about.

Billie tells me, "The police picked her up on the road three times in one week. They won't put up with it much longer." When I ask him, "Where was she going?" he replies, "She had her toothbrush and toothpaste in her pocket and she told me, 'I'm going to Texas to see Jessie.'"

201

The next day there comes an even more urgent message from Billie, "Irma was pacing back and forth in the yard for two hours and then she collapsed on the ground. Just before she collapsed, she told me, 'Look, I see Jessie coming up the driveway.' You better come quick; she's in the hospital."

Arriving in New York, I find her lying in bed, curled in the fetal position. Her skin is cold and yellow and she doesn't respond to words or touch. She looks as if she will die at any moment.

I sit in a chair next to the bed and watch her closely. When I begin to weep, she opens her eyes and looks directly at me. She moves towards me, out of herself, and struggles to make contact, but although she is still alive, she is in serious trouble.

The doctor tells me she's had a catatonic seizure because the consulting psychiatrist gave her an overdose of Haldol, a powerful tranquilizer. In addition to being catatonic, she can't hold up her head and it is resting on her sternum.

Irma peers up over the top of her glasses at the world around her. She attempts to hold conversations, but very little of what she says makes any sense. She can hardly open her mouth to eat, and she needs to be propped up, or she topples over. I'm numb with shock.

George comes from Tennessee and it seems like he can hardly bear to look at her. Aunt Gladys, her sister, and Uncle Harry come from Pennsylvania. We take Irma out of the hospital for an afternoon and have a strange family meeting in the front yard at Billie's bungalow. We sit together making small talk, trying not to admit to ourselves and to each other that something horrible is happening to one of us. Billie and George go in the house to commiserate and when they return their eyes are red.

Only Irma seems happy and content. She sits in a chair under the weeping willow covered in blankets, peering up over the top of her glasses. She loves being the center of attention and she is excited about seeing her sister again after a long separation.

When I take her to another doctor for a second opinion, he tells me the psychiatrist almost killed her with the overdose and he gives her a shot of vitamin B-12 "to get her going." Back at the hospital, the doctor tells me she is well enough to be discharged. He doesn't offer any diagnosis, nor does he give her any medication. The Haldol the psychiatrist gave her has masked her original symptoms, and no one seems to know when, or if, it will wear off.

I search for a nursing home in the area that will admit her, but I am unable to find one. Finally I'm forced to make the difficult decision to take her back to Texas with me. Billie is heartbroken, and I'm terrified of what might happen next.

The friend who drives us to the airport tells me, "I've always admired you; you're the strongest woman I know." I don't feel very strong; I feel like I'm falling apart.

At the airport, Irma becomes extremely agitated. I tie her into an airport wheelchair and wheel her back and forth. Constant movement is the only thing that seems to bring her any peace. We watch the planes take off and we eat in the restaurant where everyone stares at us, because she plays with her food like a baby.

On The Plane

Sitting in the window seat is an eighteen-year-old Puerto Rican girl with her new baby. She's taking her first trip out of New York City and her first trip on an airplane. She's going to see her husband in San Antonio.

In the middle seat is Irma, and I'm on the aisle hoping to prevent her escape. Every twenty seconds or so, Irma grabs the back of the seat in front of her, and hoisting herself upright yells, "God damn son-of-a-bitch, LET ME OUTTA HERE." I'm amazed at her violence. All her life she's played the role of the good girl and the obedient wife. Now it's as if something has removed the part of her mind that controls behavior and out comes years of pent-up rage and frustration.

The girl by the window sits in stunned silence, offering me sympathetic glances.

Hoping to calming her down, I order her old favorite, bourbon and water, mix them together, and give her a drink. She likes it, and when I'm not looking she opens the little bottle and drinks the rest of the bourbon straight. Unfortunately, it doesn't calm her down; it only makes her worse. By the time we reach Houston three and a half hours later, we're both a wreck.

We take a taxi to my apartment. At last, maybe I'll get some sleep, but that's not the way it turns out. By this time, she has become so agitated that she can't stop moving for a minute. She paces the floor incessantly, whispering to herself. After taking the knobs off the stove so she can't start a fire, I go across the street for something to eat.

I return to a nightmare: Irma, dressed only in her underwear, is crawling around on the floor like an animal. Her white hair sticks straight out and she is making weird unearthly noises and plucking at nonexistent objects on the floor. She is obviously hallucinating.

A friend goes with us to the hospital at one in the morning, and while I sit numbly in a chair in the waiting room, he walks her back and forth in the corridor.

At 2:00 a.m. they inform me they can't admit her because her Social Security number isn't registered on their computer. By 4:00 a.m. we're back in my apartment. Still she paces the floor like a caged animal. I feel like I'm going crazy right along with her.

In desperation, I go out and try to sleep in the car, but the heat and mosquitoes are merciless. At 6:00 a.m. I return to my bed and manage to sleep for three hours. When I wake up, I lock her in the apartment again and go across the street to the meditation center where I run into a friend who is a doctor. He arranges to have her admitted to a small private hospital that afternoon.

It's 1981, Irma's sixty-nine years old, and I have been forced to do the one thing I promised her I would never do, put her in the hospital and most likely a nursing home thereafter.

At the Hospital

When she's admitted, the diagnosis is "Senile dementia. Cause unknown." The hospital social worker tells me she'll take care of everything necessary to have Irma placed in a qualified nursing home after they have regulated her medication and calmed her down. What a relief it is to have someone else take over. I'm totally exhausted.

I supervise her care in the hospital as closely as I can. Since she can't speak for herself, I try to anticipate her needs and attempt to have them satisfied.

One day I arrive and find her tied in a chair, sitting in a pool of her own urine. When someone tells me she's been sitting there over four hours, I lose my temper and scream at the nurses. This is a wealthy, modern hospital in the suburbs of Houston, yet when they change her clothes, I see huge, red welts all over her buttocks – the beginnings of bed sores – that weren't there when we left New York only ten days ago. Her vulnerability has become my vulnerability. Rage and frustration consume me and I go home and cry for hours.

When the caseworker from the State Welfare Department comes to interview Irma to be certified for welfare, Irma refuses to talk to her and turns her head to the wall. Consequently she is denied welfare certification, because according to the State of Texas, Irma is not sick!

* * *

I go to the hospital to visit her, bringing a box of candy and red carnations. She is sitting up in bed when I give her my gifts. I glance away for a moment, and when I look back, I see she is eating a red carnation.

* * *

Someone from the hospital business office calls me and announces, "Ms. Bryan, you can take your mother home now; she's ready to be discharged."

"What about the nursing home your social worker promised?" I ask in disbelief, adding, "Irma doesn't have a home to go to, and besides, she's still very sick."

They explain to me that since the State of Texas has refused to certify her for Medicaid, the hospital can't afford to keep her, and no nursing home will take her, unless I can pay a thousand dollars a month, or more.

That night when I visit her she is sitting up in her bed weeping. She looks so pathetic. When she sees me, she says plaintively, "What will happen to me? Where will I go? I have nowhere to go." Instantly I realize some stupid son-of-a-bitch has been in her room discussing her situation with someone else in front of her. Don't they realize that the mind of a person with dementia is like a radio that tunes in and out? If the person happens to tune in while

205

you are discussing them, you might create more emotional damage than you'll be able to repair.

No amount of hugging and reassurance will calm her down and my inability to protect her is the most frustrating thing I've ever experienced.

Irma Goes To Mercy

My friends warn me the hospital might put her out on the street if I don't do something, so I call the Welfare Department. The person who answers the phone informs me there is one nursing home in Houston willing to take patients for the amount of their Social Security checks only, Mercy Nursing Home.

While driving over to Mercy Nursing Home, which is located in a primarily black[1] neighborhood in East Houston, I count churches. Within one square mile of the nursing home I count nine Baptist churches. They have names like Perpetual Life Missionary Baptist Church, Mt. Zion, New Evergreen, St. Emmanuel, Star Light, Church of Christ, St. Paul and Peaceful Rest Baptist Church. Included also in this square mile are Pee Wee's Icehouse: *Beer, Wine and Set-Ups*, The Continental Lounge, featuring kick-ass Louisiana Cajun music on Saturday nights, two superettes, three washaterias, several pool halls, and block after block of tiny wooden houses with no sidewalks. Some of the houses are neatly painted and have carefully tended gardens, while others have garbage and old furniture rotting in the front yard.

When I arrive at the nursing home, I'm feeling pretty frightened, but then I notice a sign over the door of the one-story brick building that reads: *Love Is Ageless*. Below these words is the painted image of an elderly woman wearing scholarly glasses. She appears to be a very kind person. Later I find out she was the founder of Mercy Nursing Home. The current administrator of Mercy is her daughter, Ms. Williams, who tells me the nursing home is usually filled to capacity and only rarely is there a bed available, but fortunately one was vacated that morning and Irma can have it.

---

[1] This story was written in the late 1980's when the term "black" was commonly used. The more appropriate term is "African American."

The next day when I drive Irma from the hospital to the nursing home, she is manageable, probably because she has been given a strong tranquilizer. She is still agitated and confused, but to a bearable degree. I attempt to be cheerful, as if going to a nursing home is the most wonderful thing that could happen to a person, but the truth is I'm terrified and wish I could bring her home with me.

When we arrive at Mercy and she realizes why we are there, she goes wild, pacing the floor of her new room and screaming. Then Delores, the activities director, comes into the room. She sits down gently on the edge of the bed next to Irma, and taking Irma's hand in hers, she says softly with a thick Southern drawl, "Now, Mz. Bryan, why you so upset?" Almost immediately, Irma begins to calm down – a process that will take nearly a year to complete – by which time she'll feel secure at Mercy and they'll be able to take her off tranquilizers.

Because of my fear that something will go wrong, I visit her almost every day. My visits are at different times during the day and night, in the hopes of finding fault with her new caretakers. But life at Mercy Nursing Home is smooth, seamless, and unchanging. The worst problem is the nasty lady in the next bed, who strikes out with a filthy sneaker whenever anyone walks by.

Ms. Williams is amazed at how agile Irma is and informs me she must walk twenty or thirty miles a day up and down the hallways. After she has been at Mercy for two weeks, I become alarmed, because her ankles and feet are swollen. Ms. Williams and I make an agreement – one I will never get used to – Irma gets restrained in a wheelchair after lunch to give her poor legs a rest.

I love Mercy Nursing Home. It doesn't look anything like a medical institution. The walls are painted various shades of bright green instead of hospital white. It's an intermediate care facility with sixty beds, and I'm glad the residents don't appear to be sick, because obvious sickness upsets Irma. Mercy is clean, but never too clean. It's friendly, homely, and rumpled. There is a color television, out-of-tune piano, pictures of Jesus, and photographs of various residents posted on the walls, as well as the monthly calendar of events.

Irma loves the backyard best. There is free access out several doors, and she seems to need this feeling of free movement. She tramples through the unkempt flowerbeds like a happy puppy and pokes at the fence that surrounds an ancient incinerator used to burn trash. The yard contains miscellaneous wooden and metal chairs and someone is always sitting in them smoking a cigarette. Occasionally the torn, weathered volleyball net is put up and Delores and the residents play ball.

After Irma has been at Mercy for three months, the Texas Welfare Department calls me to announce that now she can be moved to the nursing home of my choice, because she has been accepted for Medicaid. After visiting a more expensive home in a fancy neighborhood, and seeing the tiny, picture postcard perfect, antiseptic and unused garden, and the frozen vegetables and canned peaches they serve the residents, I tell Ms. Williams that Irma can stay at Mercy.

My favorite person at the nursing home is the cook. She makes cornbread from scratch and shops for fresh fruit and vegetables at the local farmers' market. On Sundays, if I time my visits to coincide with lunch, she'll feed me too: southern-fried chicken, greens, black-eyed peas, cornbread, and lemonade. I'd consider moving in myself, if I was a senior citizen.

When I ask Irma, "How's the food?" or "Are they taking good care of you?" she always answers with an enthusiastic, "Yes!"

Mercy Nursing Home – a haven for the helpless, sanctuary for society's unwanted, and home to Irma for as long as she needs one.

Mercy Stories

I arrive at Mercy to visit Irma, and when I get out of the car, I notice all the windows are shaking. Moving closer to the door, I hear a loud noise coming from inside. When the door opens, a wave of sound almost knocks me over. Someone is singing: "Jesus on the mainline, tell him what you want; Jesus on the mainline, tell him what you want; call him up and tell him what you want."

When I reach the dining room, I see before me an incredibly large woman. She is well over six feet tall and

208

her skin is dark and luminous. She has on a blue serge dress and a straw hat two feet wide. The sound coming out of her mouth is phenomenal. She is accompanied on electric guitar and tambourine by two young men who appear to be her sons. I can't believe my eyes. The nurse tells me joyfully, "We havin' Church!" Sho' nuff! Everyone is rockin' and rollin' in their wheelchairs, and I'm certain Jesus must be listening.

After the song is over, she sits quietly while the preacher gives a brief sermon and then we "testify." Testify means when you feel the spirit, you stand up – if you are able – and tell everyone how you feel about Jesus and what he's done for you. It's great. I feel the spirit. I want to testify too, but all I am able to do is sit quietly in the corner and weep.

Then I go and look for Irma. She's in her room, tied to a big blue chair, playing with her shoelaces. I tell them, "she loves music, be sure and bring her to Church too." I neglect to tell them, that when Irma could think, she was an atheist.

* * *

Miss Nell is the first nursing aide assigned to Irma's care and they get along great. They're the same size, and Irma cooperates with people she doesn't have to look up to. She's less inclined to be difficult when she's on equal footing with her keeper.

Miss Nell is in her sixties and has been working at Mercy for twenty-eight years. She raised five children on her own after her husband died. Miss Nell treats all the residents like they're her very own babies.

I see her most often in the morning in the bathroom, wearing a yellow-ruffled apron, up to her elbows in soapy water, giving some ornery old lady a bath. She soaps and powders them, greases and braids their hair, diapers and dresses them. Then they're ushered sweet-smelling into the dining room.

Miss Nell's babies, lined up in their wheelchairs, drinking watery gray coffee and watching television, playing cards, or just staring at the floor.

* * *

At six one morning, the night nurse calls me. She's frantic because Irma is having a seizure and demands permission to have her hospitalized immediately. Remembering my promises to a more coherent Irma to keep her out of the hospital, I ask to speak with the medic from the Emergency Care Unit who is on the scene. He tells me her seizure was probably caused by being off tranquilizers for three days. He thinks she'll be just fine once she's back on drugs, and so I refuse to give the permission necessary to put her in the hospital.

Later that day when I visit her, I find her over-medicated with Thorazine because of their fear she'll have another seizure. She keeps falling over, however, and by the end of the week, when I finally convince them to lower the dose, she has incurred two black eyes from falling on her face.

Worst of all, from my perspective, is the fact that her false teeth are not in her mouth. Since I've never seen Irma without teeth, somehow this seems symbolic of her deterioration. Miss Nell and I get in the washroom, together with the false teeth and Irma, and try to coax her to open her mouth and embrace the teeth. No way. Her jaw is firmly shut against all invaders, and she is quite stubborn. Finally, in desperation, Miss Nell looks towards the ceiling, holding the teeth in her hand, and exclaims, "PLEASE JESUS, LET IT OPEN." Instantly Irma's jaw drops, and Nell pops in the teeth. Another battle in the fight for normalcy has been won.

* * *

By the time Irma takes up residence in her small room at Mercy Nursing Home, her earthly possessions are somewhat reduced. The stereo, records, and paintings are being used in George's family room. Everything else is either dumped in the utility room of his garage or with Billie, who is still hoping for a miraculous recovery and her return to New York. Irma's one piece of gold jewelry, a ring inherited from her mother, has been given to George's daughter.

She brings with her to Mercy a gray plastic suitcase holding miscellaneous clothing, photographs, and an old straw purse filed with cheap dime store jewelry. The

210

clothing goes in the closet after being marked with her name and the photographs go on the wall. There is a large picture of me, age four, curtsying before the camera, a picture of a woman from Irma's past of some forgotten importance, one of my brother, age ten, in a stripped tee-shirt, and one of Irma in her nightgown holding me when I was a baby. Also on the wall is a two foot valentine sent by her sister Gladys, who keeps writing me asking, "Is Irma feeling better yet?"

Knowing the jewelry will most likely get lost I decide we should have some fun giving it away. We go up to each old lady in the dining room, and Irma gives her a necklace, ring, or bracelet. For at least two weeks, everyone is happily showing off her new jewelry. Irma keeps, among other items, a white plastic clip-on bracelet with her initials, "I.B." At this point in her life, I guess she occasionally remembers her name is "Irma Bryan."

The last item to come out of the suitcase is the "duck." It is only a piece of driftwood, but it is shaped remarkably like a duck. It is her most treasured possession, acquired in happier times during a camping trip to Green Bay, Wisconsin when I was nine years old and Irma was a vibrant forty-two. It sits silently on the table next to her bed, an obscure reminder of our lifetime together. Eventually, one of the nursing aides gets tired of cleaning around it and throws it away, but by that time Irma no longer seems to care.

* * *

Irma has a friend at Mercy named Laura Jones. Laura's face is dark, round, and soft and she is always smiling. She is very thin and a foot taller than Irma. Her old-fashioned dresses hang limply around her bony knees. Laura loves to walk the hallways too, and she and Irma spend hours together holding hands, talking nonsense, and walking.

One sunny afternoon, I decide to take them both to a small beach on the San Marcos River about forty-five minutes south of Houston. They are excited about the prospect of an outing, although neither of them seems to remember exactly what a beach is.

When we arrive at the river, I park near the sand and open the car doors so they can get out. Irma immediately

211

bolts out of the car, running as fast as she can towards the water. Laura Jones however, steps out gingerly, testing the sand beneath her bare feet. She walks as if she's on a boat, rocking back and forth, cautiously, slowly, and exclaiming all the while, "Why I ain't never, I ain't never, I ain't never been no where's like this befo." She's either never been to a beach, or has forgotten if she was. We make it to the shore, where Laura sits on the blanket gazing placidly at the water, while I restrain Irma from falling in. Laura refuses to speak, shocked by the alien environment, and Irma soon quiets down in this peaceful place. We have apple juice and peanut butter sandwiches for lunch and then head for home.

On the freeway the old Dodge blows a hose and spews water all over the road. While it's being repaired, Irma and I go into a restaurant for tea and scrambled eggs, where she embarrasses me by yelling at the waitress. Laura Jones refuses to get out of the car and falls asleep on the back seat.

By the time we arrive back at Mercy an hour later, they've both forgotten where we went!

* * *

Irma's glasses are never on her face where they belong. The nursing station? Yes! Her bedside table? Yes! Under the bed? Yes! Out in the yard, half-buried in the dirt? Yes! But never on her face, never where they belong.

I plead with the head nurse, Ms. Williams, Miss Nell, the cook, and the woman who does the laundry. I tape notes to her bed, the wall, and the closet doors saying, *Please Put On Irma's Glasses,* but to no avail. It's infuriating. Don't they realize her sight is very poor, and considering the tranquilizers she takes and the way she runs up and down the hallways, she could break her neck at any moment.

My efforts are in vain, however, because Irma herself is working against me, and in her innocence, she is an insurmountable foe. She takes them off when no one is looking and discards them wherever she happens to be.

After two years of constant struggle (and after she breaks two new pairs in one week), I give up all efforts on behalf of her glasses.

Irma is standing in the corridor at Mercy looking totally lost. Her eyes are clouded over. She turns to me, and for a moment the cloud lifts and consciousness lights her eyes.

"I'm dying aren't I?" she asks, as a look of terror crosses her face.

Before I can answer, she's gone again, and I'm thankful for the memory loss that protects her from her fear of death.

* * *

Ms. Johnson, the head nurse, calls me one afternoon, "Mz. Bryan, I'm sorry to tell you, but your mother's got a black eye."

I go right over, and sure enough, Irma's got a shiner like you wouldn't believe. I question Ms. Williams and Ms. Johnson, but get nowhere. All they will say is, "It's an isolated incident; we're sure it will <u>never</u> happen again."

I'm suspicious because their smiles do not seem sincere. Perhaps some other patient has it in for Irma, especially since she's always wandering in and out of the other residents' rooms and rummaging through their belongings. Finally I give up on getting a straight answer and head towards the door where I run into Delores. "Oh say." Wasn't that something about Irma!" she exclaims, and laughs like crazy.

I stay real cool, "Ah, what happened?"

"Well," she says, "It's like this. Two of the patients was out in the garden and they was, well, in a romantic mood. Irma goes out there and starts a fussin' at them, and they gits mad and gives her a punch, and that's how she got that big ol' shiner."

We laugh so hard we collapse breathless into each other's arms.

* * *

My best friend Cindy agrees to take our picture, and so one afternoon we pose out in her backyard. When the pictures are developed, I frame one and take it over to the nursing home. In the picture Irma and I are standing close

213

together and I have my arm around her. She is wearing a lavender dress and looks really tiny next to me. We are both beaming at the camera.

I give Irma the picture in the frame and pointing to myself ask, "Look, Irma, who's that?"

She replies without hesitation, "That's my mother; she takes good care of me."

In disbelief, I ask her again, "Irma, who's that in the picture?" and she replies, "Oh, she's a very nice person."

I remember the time before she got sick, when she belittled me, accused me, and denied me her love and approval. I begin to understand we've been playing roles, but now those roles are no longer appropriate.

We're both becoming someone else, but we haven't yet recognized who we are.

* * *

Irma and I are riding in Cindy's car. It's an old heap with no hood over the engine, bald tires, and a missing rear view mirror. It's also a standard transmission, which I'm not used to driving. In attempting to pull out at a stoplight, I pop the clutch and stall out the engine three times. We end up sitting through two red and green lights, as I frantically try to get the old heap moving.

I turn towards Irma and make excuses for my apparent failure, "I'm sorry for the delay; I'm not used to driving this kind of car." She is not listening, however, or paying any attention at all to my driving. She is gazing out the window, a perfect picture of tranquility and blissful ignorance of what's happening around her. I'm stunned by the realization that I'm still playing the role of the criticized child, but she's not playing "mommie" anymore.

* * *

When Irma began to lose her ability to communicate, she began to lose her ability to criticize. When she stopped talking completely, she could no longer verbally abuse me the way she had in the past. In this way, the tragedy of her illness was also a blessing for both of us. When she stopped criticizing me, I was able to love her, especially since she became more and more like an adorable child.

214

When I was able to show my love for her, she stopped needing to criticize me, and the neurotic pattern we had been involved in for years was forever altered. Our relationship began to heal. The more I fell in love with her, the more I fell in love with myself, and now I realize the destructive things she said and did when I was a child had little to do with me – but rather, they were reflections of her own poor self-esteem and distorted view of her role as a mother.

* * *

Delores has organized another party in the newly painted and redecorated dining room. The residents are lined up in neat rows and none of them are asleep. There's a six piece jazz ensemble with a terrific saxophone player wailing away on *Shake, Rattle and Roll.* Laura Jones is hopping up and down in her chair so hard I'm afraid she'll either fall out and break a leg or have a coronary! Delores laughs and tells me, "Why say chil' look at that Laura Jones, and she's supposed to be one church-saved woman too." One old man starts to cry and tells me it's because he remembers when he was a trumpet player before he had a stroke; the music brings back too many memories. Wearing an electric blue dress and red high heels, Delores jumps up and swings him around the room to take his mind off his troubles. We pass out punch and chocolate cake. Irma tries to stick her fingers in my mouth and shakes her legs in time to the music.

* * *

Irma and I sit quietly against the wall in the dining room holding hands. Her fingers seem tiny and vulnerable in mine. During the course of our attempted conversation, she calls me by my name, "Jessie," for the first time in two years. Today is Christmas, and it's the only and best present she can give me.

Mercy is hectic and crowded for the holiday celebration. Families and various church groups are passing out presents for the residents, who seem confused by the uproar and extra attention.

Irma and I leave and go downtown to our favorite Mexican restaurant, where we have chicken enchiladas for our Christmas dinner. What a mess she makes of the table. By the time we are finished eating, there are fifteen soiled napkins lying around and everything in sight is covered with cheese and tomato sauce. We are satiated and totally contented.

At dinner I ask her, "Have you seen Jessie lately?" and she answers, "I always did like little Jessie."

* * *

Keeping track of her clothes becomes my daily obsession, because the clothes that aren't ruined by harsh laundry soap invariably end up on the backs of the wrong residents. Every few months I go to the thrift store and buy Irma six or seven new dresses, only to arrive a week later to find other residents wearing them. Irma herself is often wearing someone else's rags.

The women who do the laundry either can't or won't read the names on the doors of the closets and nothing is ever in the right place. The nursing aides dress the residents in whatever they find in the closet. I can go to Mercy any day of the week and find twenty or thirty items belonging to someone else in Irma's closet, and her beautiful dresses are nowhere to be seen.

This problem is partially surmounted by purchasing everything in some shade of pink, including her washable sneakers. After awhile, everyone begins to associate Irma with pink, and I find her wearing her own clothes more often.

* * *

We're going shopping! Well actually we're going to a "swap" sponsored by the Unity Church. A "swap" is where you bring anything you don't want and trade it for something else.

When we arrive at the church, I see that most of the participants have brought clothing. There are racks and racks of it set up in the parking lot. After unloading our contribution from my car, Irma and I go from rack to rack like indulgent children. I hold up each garment that looks like it might fit her and ask, "Would you like to have this one?" Her face is red with excitement as she yells, "YES!" Soon we are both carrying as many articles of clothing as we possibly can, and we collapse exhausted and spent on a bench.

I have never seen her so happy. She has a new dress for every day of two weeks. All her life she scrimped and saved for everything. Now in her old age, it's total abundance.

* * *

Our next shopping trip wasn't so much fun. One Saturday morning, we go to a thrift store located in the barrio where I live. When we get into the store, Irma refuses to participate. She keeps trying to run out of the door, tears through the racks of clothing, and yells at me. Although I attempt to assuage her with the promise of new dresses, she's unable to cooperate.

So I do something I've done before with no problems, I put her in the car, lock the door, roll down the window, and tell her at least ten times, "Sit here and be a good girl. I'll be right back." She nods complacently and I return to shopping. About ten minutes later, after I have picked out several nice dresses and paid for them, I return to the car, which is parked just outside the front door of the store.

THE CAR DOOR IS WIDE OPEN AND IRMA IS NOWHERE TO BE SEEN! Evidently she remembered how to manipulate the door handle, and recognizing a chance for freedom, she took off.

I begin to run in circles in the parking lot screaming and crying, "I'VE LOST IRMA! I'VE LOST IRMA!" When I come to my senses, I run back into the store and call the police and the nursing home. I also call Cindy, who although she has been up all night with her boyfriend, is out the door to our rescue in five seconds. Within ten minutes, Cindy and I, the police, and several volunteers from the nursing home are cruising the neighborhood looking for Irma.

We pull up alongside five or six ragged fellows, who are lying on the sidewalk drinking wine, and ask them, "Did you see a short old lady with white hair, wearing a yellow dress and pink satin slippers go by here?"

"Sure," they reply. "She went that way."

We turn the corner, but she's nowhere to be found. For over an hour, Cindy and I drive around looking for her, and then it begins to rain. You know, the kind of rain they have in South Texas, a downpour, almost a flood. By this time, I'm contemplating suicide. I can't bear the thought of what might happen to her. I imagine trying to tell George I lost his mother in a rainstorm and threaten to hurl myself out of the car window.

Cindy calms me down by taking me to Andy's Cafe, where we have rice and beans, and then she drives me home. I'm lying on the bed, feeling totally defeated by my "Life With Irma," when the phone rings. "Mz. Bryan, we just wanted to tell you the police brought your mother home a few minutes ago."

I jump back into the car and drive over to Mercy where the head nurse tells me, "The policeman who brought her home told us he found her playing in a rain puddle near a housing project with a group of children." She reprimands me for letting Irma get wet and for letting the pink satin slippers get ruined in the rain, because they belong to another resident. She doesn't seem to care that Irma got lost, only that she got wet! They are so concerned about her catching a cold that they have bundled her up in blankets and tied her in bed.

When I go to her room, she is very excited to see me; her face is bright red. After yelling at her for a few minutes about running away, I ask her, "Well, honey, did you enjoy yourself? Was it fun?"

With an ecstatic look on her face, she answers, "I lika, lika, lika, lika, lika, lika," which probably means she had fun. It also seems she is upset the fun is over."

* * *

Irma's seventieth birthday is approaching. Since her birthday falls just two days before Christmas, she has never had a real birthday party. I intend to give her a great party, because it may be her last birthday.

Cindy and I bake a huge chocolate cake with chocolate icing. It's big enough for the sixty residents and all the staff at the nursing home. We write *Happy Birthday, Irma* on it with red frosting. Her presents will be pink socks, pink sneakers, and a big teddy bear.

The day of the party finally arrives. The dining room is filled with brightly colored balloons, and everyone is sitting around waiting for the party to begin. We sing *Happy Birthday* and pass out the presents. The party is for all of the residents with a birthday in December, but everyone else gets a present too. The men get a pair of socks and the women small bottles of perfume, compliments of the nursing home. Irma is not the slightest bit interested in presents; all she cares about is cake, and since she is sitting right in front of a huge cake, she keeps sticking her fingers in the icing. There is no threat terrible enough to keep her fingers out of the icing. It's just too irresistible.

After the presents are opened, we cut the cake. Now she has what she wants the most. She sits there quietly eating cake throughout the rest of the party. She eats at least ten pieces.

Next on the agenda is entertainment, and I'm it. In honor of the birthday party, I've learned several Negro spirituals, because I want the audience to be able to relate to the music. This is one of the most difficult audiences I've ever encountered. There is a wide generation gap, and of course, the color and cultural gap. I stumble through *Swing Low Sweet Chariot, Amazing Grace*, and *May The Circle Be Unbroken*," playing my guitar and singing much too fast. Although the audience tries to sing along, they can't speed up, and I can't seem to slow down, try as I might. When I get to the last song, I'm really upset. From my perspective, this performance is ruining a perfectly planned party.

When I start to sing the last song, *He's Got The Whole World In His Hands*, Delores steps in and saves me by singing along loudly at the right speed. Suddenly everyone is singing with great feeling. This must be their favorite song. When it reaches a hand-clapping, roaring crescendo, everyone is satisfied, and the party has been an overwhelming success.

Then something happens to one lady who is over ninety years old and blind. She has soft, honey-colored skin with a multitude of freckles and long braids wound about her head. She sits bent over in her wheelchair like a fiddlehead – the ones you see in a forest – a fern leaf that hasn't uncurled yet towards the sun. As I'm watching her, she slowly begins to uncurl. As she grows taller in her chair, coming fully to life, she begins to sing in a strong, plaintive voice, "Oh how I love Jesus, oh how I love Jesus, because...he...first...loved me."

As I feel the love that pours from her heart, I remember the words of Swami Muktananda: "You are not the physical body – the body that grows old, decays, and dies. You are pure love, the pure love that is God in each human heart. You are the perfect Self, and the Self never dies."

* * *

I arrive at the nursing home bringing an Eskimo Pie and find her sitting on the bed in her room while the nursing aide dresses her in blue jeans, tee shirt, and hot pink sneakers. There are bruises on both of her forearms, presumably the result of bumping into things. She is chewing rapidly with her three remaining teeth on a wadded up piece of paper napkin left over from lunch. When I say, "Hi, Irma," she doesn't look up or respond in any way. I get down in front of her face for closer viewing, but she stares at me as if I don't exist. I hold the ice cream in front of her mouth and it opens mechanically. The mouth grabs the ice cream and swallows it in three bites.

Then we walk. She moves forward in any arbitrary direction until she encounters an object, and then she moves around it, staring at the floor, perhaps watching her feet. She doesn't force anything to conform to her movement, but when something gets in her way, she mumbles with disgust or exclaims, "NO!" and then walks around it. Where is she going? Why is she constantly moving? Even after all this time, it's still a mystery.

We go outside and walk around the neighborhood. When I try to bring her back inside, she clings to the doorway resisting entry. Finally she enters the building and heads down the hallway towards the nursing station, while I walk towards the dining room, which vibrates with the sound of joyful singing.

Sister Leroy, Reverend Washington, and the Deacon are having "Church" and I rejoice at my good timing to arrive for this moving event. It's quite a scene. Reverend Washington is bellowing out his sermon. He looks like an overweight ballet dancer, rocking from foot to foot, waving

220

his arms in the air, his voice rising and falling, majestically praising God. He tells the congregation, "In hell it's too late to pray. It's gittin' late in the evening and our sun is going down. Repent and do God's Will." The air is vibrant with "Yes, Yes! Amen! That's Right!" and "Praise Jesus!" as some of the audience respond in affirmation. A large portion of the audience, however, doesn't seem to care at all about "Church." They're asleep upright in their chairs with their mouths open, dozing after the noonday meal. Others nod their heads rhythmically, wave their arms, or bang their hands on the tables.

When the sermon is finished, Sister Leroy jumps up, grabs Laura Jones, and dances her around in circles as she explodes in song:

> When the war is over, we shall wear a crown;
> When the battle's over, we shall wear a crown;
> When our trials are over, we shall wear a crown,
> in the New Jerusalem.

Just then Irma wanders into the room, criss-crossing back and forth, tilting slightly to the left. In one hand, she is clutching a battered magazine, and in the other, a blue blanket and white sheet still neatly folded together, taken from someone's bed. With the blanket and sheet trailing eight feet behind her, she looks both adorable and totally pathetic and my heart bursts open with love and compassion.

Then one very old man, who has been staring at me lasciviously and blowing kisses throughout the whole program, begins to "testify," tears running silently down his cheeks. Sister Leroy hugs everyone in the room and we sing, "I'm so glad Jesus lives in me," and "Till we meet again at Jesus' feet." Church is over.

I realize she no longer needs me. What held us together no longer exists. Irma's forgotten she ever had a daughter, and I feel both useless and relieved. Mercy gives her everything she needs and there is nothing more for me to do except accept her as the person she becomes in each moment and hope that when her trials are over, Irma too will wear a "crown" in the "New Jerusalem."

Epilogue: What Happened To Billie

Billie's moved uptown to downtown Monticello, and it's first class all the way. He pays $50 a month for a two-bedroom apartment that's so clean you could eat off the linoleum. He has new furniture, throw rugs, dishes, sheets, blankets – everything in the whole apartment is new – and I soon find out why it's so clean.

Billie has a woman for every day of the week. He proudly shows me a letter from the Sullivan County Welfare Department authorizing him for homemaker services seven days a week, five hours a day. He tells me his favorite one is "the little Irish girl." They play poker and once a week she takes him to Mass at the Catholic Church. She has given him a miniature Christmas tree with tiny lights and it sits on the table next to his bed.

Billie also has a new bathroom. Unlike the shower at the bungalow, this bathroom has hot running water and a tub you can actually bathe in. There is a fire engine red shower curtain and matching rugs and toilet seat cover. The women from the Welfare Department bathe and shave him, as well as cook, clean, and do the laundry. The kitchen is immaculate, and so is Billie. He's wearing clean pants and the dirty dishes are carefully piled up on the counter waiting for the woman of the day who will wash them.

Billie cries about losing me, Irma, and his "puppies" (who were not allowed to move with him into his new apartment), and then he regales me with stories about the women he meets on the bench in front of Woolworth's, weather permitting. These are "classy dames" he insists. They are also big drinkers, and he is pleased to spend his money on them.

According to Billie, life at seventy-six is not so bad. He plays the pinball machines at the bus station and courts the three widows who live in his building. His closet is crammed with new suits and shoes, purchased with the money he's saving on rent.

He gives me fatherly advice: "Now listen, Jessie, when you gonna settle down and get married?"

"I'll settle down and get married when I find the right man," I explain, but he doesn't understand my logic.

"No man wants a woman with wings on her feet. You've got 'em just like me, you <u>need</u> to settle down."

Finally, to shut him up, I tell him, "Well, I can always get married when I'm ninety years old!" He looks at me like he thinks I'm crazy.

Three years ago I bought him a cardboard turkey for Thanksgiving and Billie still has it hanging on the wall. Beneath it hangs a plastic bride and groom, the kind you put on a wedding cake. They're from Woolworth's and cost him $2.59. He takes them down carefully and gives them to me saying, "You keep this for when you get married, and be sure to think of me." The tenderness in his voice almost makes me cry.

Also hanging on the wall is a picture of Irma in her mid-thirties diapering me when I was a baby. When the Irish "girl" asked him if he was married, he told her, "Yes, but the baby is almost forty years old now." In Billie's mind, Irma and I are the family he never had. He wishes it so fervently, that in his old age it's come true, if only in his mind. "Memories, that's all I have now," he tells me sadly.

"What about the women who come to visit you and do the housework, aren't they company?" I ask. He replies, "It's not the same as you and Irma – I loved your mother; she made me laugh."

Just then the doorbell rings and the woman of the day arrives. Fussing over her noisily, he forgets me completely and hardly notices when I slip out the door.

SIMPLY MUST
Juley Harvey

there are few enough
things we can do in life
but to love one other person
with all our days
totally, fully, without
count of cost or wrath
at god or ire or grief
remains the simple star
without which we would be lost,
on which we hang all soaring
hopes and belief.
no matter how forgetful the future,
it's this remembrance that we praise.
for we can watch, but never know
what happens to those
we must somehow let go.
so we stand by them or perish,
as surely as if it were our own malady,
past all love and lust – it's not even
a case of choose to, but one
of simply must.

ST. LUKE'S GARDEN
Lillian Waller, Age 91

This park is a favorite place
a personal place
It is a place of beauty

It is a park of poems
I call it
the squirrel and his love

Here you don't have to
figure things out
You can't figure things out

Beauty can almost never be completely repeated
The beautiful design of the tree cannot be repeated
The beauty that we saw today cannot be repeated

The beauty is here
but if you don't realize it
then it can't be there

I came from nowhere
and I went to everywhere
No, there's no other place like this

It's there for God's sake
and that's that

ALZHEIMER'S DISEASE

Alzheimer's disease is a progressive, irreversible, neurological disorder that affects an estimated four million middle-aged and elderly Americans, although it can also strike a person in his or her 40s. It affects one in ten over age 65 and one-half over age 85. As the population grows and more people live longer, the projected number of those afflicted is expected to grow to 14 million by the year 2050. It is the most common form of dementing illness and the fourth leading cause of death in adults. Persons with Alzheimer's disease are also referred to as having "senile dementia." *Webster's Unabridged Dictionary* defines "senile" as "a syndrome of progressive, irreversible impairment of cognitive function, caused by organic factors, and having its onset late in life," and "dementia" as "a condition of deteriorated mentality." Over 50% of all senile dementia is caused by Alzheimer's.

Although symptoms of senile dementia have been documented since before the time of Christ, it was in 1906 that Alois Alzheimer, a German psychiatrist and neuropathologist, discovered the presence of twisted nerve-cell fibers (which he called "neurofibrillary tangles") in the brain tissue of a fifty-one year old woman. For decades it was thought to be a rare condition confined to the relatively young, but then in the 1960's researchers using electron microscopes discovered these same neurofibrillary tangles in the brain tissue of elderly patients suffering from dementia. These tangles form in and around brain nerve cells, blocking the transportation of nutrients and cutting off neuron messages. The brain also starts producing abnormal amounts of a protein called amyloid that deposits sticky plaque between the nerve cells and clogs up the blood vessels. This combination of tangles and plaque erodes the functioning of the brain resulting in dementia.

Before a tentative diagnosis of Alzheimer's disease can be made, it is important to rule out other causes of dementia, some of which can be treated, such as: depression, multiple minor strokes, brain tumors, adverse drug reactions, metabolic changes, infections, Parkinson's disease, anemia, arteriosclerosis, hypo-thyroidism, drug reactions, dehydration, advanced syphilis, alcoholism, and poor diet in combination with malabsorption of nutrients.

Alzheimer's is identified by a gradual, but steady decline in cognitive functioning over a period of 2-10 years. One of the first symptoms, forgetfulness, often goes unnoticed. Those afflicted become absentminded and lose their spontaneity and the ability to discriminate. Many are easily angered and may become inappropriate in social situations. As the disease progresses, they have difficulty making decisions and performing previously understood tasks. They may become insensitive to the feelings of others and avoid situations that are challenging, out of fear of failure.

As the disease worsens, Alzheimer's patients show an obvious loss of memory and judgment. They become lost if they go out alone. They can no longer read or understand movies and television programs. They can't find the words they want to use and may invent words. They usually identify incorrectly people they previously knew. While their short-term memory deteriorates, their memory of long past people and events is often less affected.

As they move into the final stages of Alzheimer's disease, they become totally disoriented in relation to time, people, places, and objects. For example, they may stop eating because they no longer understand how to use utensils or what the purpose of food is. They involve themselves in repetitive actions and may not recognize their own families or their own names.

Advanced Alzheimer's patients often become incontinent and need to wear diapers. They may live in the distant past and hallucinate. They may be angry, fearful, or extremely passive. They may speak only two or three words, or not at all. Although the body may still be moving, the brain has failed, and eventually they fall into a coma and die of pneumonia, a stroke, urinary tract infections or other complications common to bedridden elderly patients.

There is much that is unknown about Alzheimer's disease, but it is known to be irreversible, incurable, and not related to sex, race or socio-economic factors. Some of the possible causes and potential cures or preventatives being investigated are:

Neurotransmitters: It is believed that the memory loss in Alzheimer's patients results from the lack of neurotransmitters (which are responsible for transmitting thoughts) in combination with the presence of neuritic plaques (knobby patches of dying nerve fibers), neurofibrillary tangles (twisted nerve-cell fibers), and reduced blood flow.

Neurotransmitters transmit electrical impulses in the brain and are responsible for transmitting thoughts and feelings. The discovery that Alzheimer's patients have a deficiency in the neurotransmitter acetylcholine has prompted researchers to test drugs that can raise its levels. Drugs currently in use include Aricept and Reminyl, which increase levels of acetylcholine by blocking the action of an enzyme that normally removes it from the brain.

Toxins: At one time aluminum was thought to be either a possible cause or the result of Alzheimer's disease. This theory is currently out of favor, as testing done on workers in aluminum mines found no such connection. (See *Archives of Neurology,* May 1998.)

The brain tissue of people with Alzheimer's has been found to contain higher than normal amounts of mercury. Therefore, mercury exposure from dental amalgams and other sources cannot be excluded as a possible contributor.

Blood Flow: At one time, senile dementia was blamed on hardening of the arteries, but this is no longer the case. However, in an Alzheimer's patient there is a definite reduction in the amount of oxygen and glucose available for utilization by the brain. This reduction increases as the disease progresses. The herb ginkgo biloba may be of some treatment value, because it acts as an antioxidant and increases blood flow to the brain. (See *Journal of the American Medical Association,* October 22, 1977.)

Virus or Other Infectious Agents: Scientists have discovered several other diseases similar to Alzheimer's that are caused by a slow virus. They have been able to transmit these diseases to laboratory animals, but thus far have been unable to transmit Alzheimer's and thereby study it further.

Genetics: Many Alzheimer's patients have a family history of the disease. It is believed that approximately ten

228

percent of the patients with Alzheimer's have inherited it. If a family member is afflicted, it is more likely that other family members will get it too. The younger the relative is when contracting the disease, the greater the risk to the other family members. Predictive genetic testing is available, but usually only for individuals who have a family member who got the disease before age 60. Four different genes have been linked to the disease, and although these discoveries may not produce a cure or preventative measure in the near future, scientists believe the long-range possibilities are favorable.

Inflammation and COX-2 Inhibition: Malfunction of the immune system is responsible for many illnesses in which the immune system attacks the body's own tissues. Proteins resulting from such attacks have been found in and around the plaques and tangles in the brains of people who have died of Alzheimer's.

There is evidence that COX-2 inhibitors reduce inflammation of the brain, and thus it is possible they might reduce the damage caused by Alzheimer's. In addition to the pharmaceutical COX-2 inhibitors, many natural supplements are available that can reduce inflammation, including: rosemary, turmeric, gota kola, green tea, Chinese Goldthread, Barberry, Basil, Skullcap, Huzhang, ginger, oregano, feverfew, hops, and others. For a complete discussion of this theory please see *Beyond Aspirin: Nature's Answer to Arthritis, Cancer and Alzheimer's Disease* by Thomas M. Newmark and Paul Schulick.

Plasma Homocysteine as a Risk Factor for Dementia and Alzheimer's Disease: Recent research by Sudha Seshadri, M.D. et al. shows that an increased plasma homocysteine level is a strong, independent risk factor for the development of Alzheimer's disease. It can be hypothesized from this research that it might be possible to prevent or ameliorate Alzheimer's by keeping your homocysteine levels in check. A simple blood test can determine homocysteine levels. Eating a diet rich in fruits and vegetables and taking vitamin supplements B6, B-12, and folic acid are effective in addressing elevated homocysteine levels. *The New England Journal of Medicine*, Vol. 346, No. 7, pp. 476-483, February 14, 2002 and AARP *Bulletin*, p.15, April 2002. *See* also, Gottlieb, S. (2002). Higher folic acid levels could reduce risk of Alzheimer's.

BMJ Vol. 324, pp. 441-441; *Journal of Neurochemistry*, 2002, Vol., 80, pp.101-110; and the Institute of Health Sciences, which can be found at: www.hsibaltimore.com.

Vitamin deficiency: In addition to B6, B12, and folic acid, which address elevated homocysteine levels, other vitamins and nutrients may be helpful in the treatment and prevention of Alzheimer's disease. In particular, the development of neurofibrillary tangles and amyloid plaques found in people with Alzheimer's has been associated with zinc deficiency. (See, *PRESCRIPTION FOR NUTRITIONAL HEALING* James F. Balch, M.D. and Phyllis A. Balch, CNC.)

Until a cure or preventative measure for Alzheimer's is found, good planning can ease the burden on patients and family members. Respite care for primary caregivers is especially important. Carefully prescribed medication can lessen the patient's agitation, anxiety, and unpredictable behavior, as well as improve sleeping patterns and help depression. Physical exercise, social activity, proper nutrition, and medical care are also important.

Placement in residential care, such as a nursing home, adult family home, or other type of assisted living facility, is often necessary as the disease progresses. It helps to think about this possibility in advance, rather than waiting until the last minute, as some facilities have waiting lists. Placement can often be a very positive move for someone with dementia.

By keeping the environment calm and well-structured, perhaps Alzheimer's patients may retain some measure of dignity and comfort.

Keep informed of current research developments by visiting this web site: www.alzforum.org.

RESOURCES

Alzheimer's Disease Education and Referral Center,
National Institute on Aging
P.O. Box 8250, Silver Spring, MD 20907-8250
(800) 438-4380: Toll free information and referral line.
www.alzheimer's.org

ADEAR is a service of the federal government's National Institute On Aging (NIA). The Center provides accurate, up-to-date information about Alzheimer's disease and related disorders to patients and their families, caregivers, health care providers, and the public. It operates a toll-free information and referral line from 8:30 a.m. to 5:00 p.m., Eastern Standard Time, Monday through Friday. Callers can get answers to basic questions about Alzheimer's disease, caregiving, research findings, and treatment studies; free publications; and, referrals to other organizations for additional information and services. ADEAR provides an extensive bibliographic database on its web site.

Alzheimer's Association
919 N. Michigan Avenue, Suite 1100
Chicago, IL 60611-1676
(800) 272-3900
www.alz.org

The Alzheimer's Association has a national network of chapters and is the largest national voluntary health organization committed to finding a cure for Alzheimer's disease and helping those afflicted with the disease. The Association provides education and support to people diagnosed with Alzheimer's, caregivers, health care professionals, researchers, or media. The Association is the top private funder of research into the causes, treatments, prevention, and cure of Alzheimer's disease and has been awarded more than $100 million in research grants. It is possible to obtain education materials from the Association's comprehensive library.

BIBLIOGRAPHY

The following is a partial list of the books available on the subject of Alzheimer's disease and healing in general. Please refer to the two organizations on the preceding page for more information.

THE FORGETTING, Alzheimer's: Portrait of an Epidemic
David Shenk, Doubleday, New York, 2001

THE 36-HOUR DAY
Nancy L. Mace, M.A. and Peter V. Robins, M.D., 3rd Ed.
The John Hopkins University Press, Baltimore, 1999

ALZHEIMER'S FINDING THE WORDS: A Communication Guide For Those Who Care, Harriet Dogson
John Wiley & Songs, Inc., New York

ANOTHER COUNTRY: Navigating The Emotional Terrain of Our Elders, Mary Pipher, Ph.D.
Riverhead Books, New York, 1999

THE LOSS OF SELF: A Family Resource for the Care of Alzheimer's Disease and Related Disorders
D. Cohen and C. Eisdorfer, New York: Norton, 1986

COUNTING ON KINDNESS: The Dilemmas of Dependency,
Free Press, Simon & Schuster, 1991
TAKING CARE OF AGING FAMILY MEMBERS: A Practical Guide, Free Press, Simon & Schuster, 1993
Wendy Lustbader:

PRESCRIPTION FOR NUTRITIONAL HEALING
James F. Balch, M.D. and Phyllis A. Balch, CNC
Penguin Putnam, New York, 2000
This is a practical reference book regarding the use of vitamins, minerals, herbs and food supplements. It includes a comprehensive chapter regarding Alzheimer's disease.

BEYOND ASPIRIN: NATURE'S ANSWER TO ARTHRITIS,
CANCER & ALZHEIMER'S DISEASE
Thomas M. Newmark and Paul Schulick, Hohm Press 2000

Web sites that provide information on non-conventional
cognitive enhancement products: www.hepmed.com;
www.inhome-health.com; and www.hfn-usa.com

LOVE, MEDICINE & MIRACLES, Harper Perennial, 1990
PRESCRIPTIONS FOR LIVING, Harper Collins, 1998
Bernie Siegel, M.D.

FORGIVENESS, The Greatest Healer of All, LOVE IS LETTING
GO OF FEAR, and *TEACH ONLY LOVE: The Twelve*
Principles of Attitudinal Healing Gerald G. Jampolsky, M.D.
Available at www.healingcenter.org., (888) 222-7202, and
www.Amazon.com

A YEAR TO LIVE: How To Live This Year As If It Were Your
Last, Three Rivers Press, 1998
WHO DIES? An Investigation of Conscious Living and
Conscious Dying, Anchor, New York, 1989
MEETINGS AT THE EDGE – Conversations With the Grieving
and the Dying, the Healing and the Healed, Doubleday, New
York, 1984, Stephen and Ondrea Levine

SYMPHONY OF SPIRITS: Encounters With the Spiritual
Dimension of Alzheimer's
Deborah A. Forrest, Ph.D., with Clint Richmond
St. Martin's Press, New York, 2000

ON DEATH AND DYING, Scriber, New York, 1997
ON LIFE AFTER DEATH, Celestial Arts, Berkeley, 1991
Elizabeth Kubler-Ross

AGELESS DESIGN: (561) 745-0210
Ageless Design provides information on products for safety
in the home and other solutions for living with Alzheimer's
disease.

ACKNOWLEDGEMENTS, PERMISSIONS, AND AUTHOR BIOGRAPHIES

All of the stories and poems in this anthology are reprinted with the permission of the authors. Some appeared in the 1st Edition of *Love Is Ageless*, but many appear here for the first time.

CALLE ESPAÑA © 1987 Eduardo A. Alvarez, M.D.

Eduardo A. Alvarez was born in the Dominican Republic where he graduated medical school in 1938. He practiced medicine in Brooklyn, N.Y. for many years and is a "Completed Fellow" of the American College of Surgeons.

TESTING STARS © 1987 Jan Bailey

Jan Bailey is the author of *Paper Clothes* (Emrys Press) and *Heart of the Other: Island Poems* (Two Fish Press). Her poems have appeared in *The Kenyon Review, Ploughshares, The South Carolina Review, Nimrod International,* and *Spoon River Poetry,* among others. A resident of Maine, Ms. Bailey currently serves as Chair of the Creative Writing Department at the South Carolina Governor's School for the Arts and Humanities in Greenville, South Carolina.

IT'S ONLY MAKE BELIEVE © 2002 Barbara Beckman

Barbara Beckman lives in Minnesota with her dog Riley. A freelance writer, short-story writer, and columnist (under the pen name Evelyn Pulver), she continues to work one evening a week as a nursing home assistant in a neighborhood nursing home. She's currently writing a book about shut-ins who lead full lives. Know of any? E-mail her at beckman@i29.net.

TECHNICAL DIFFICULTY © 1988 Ronnie R. Brown

Technical Difficulty was previously published in *Decisive Moments* by Ronnie R. Brown (Anthos Books: Valley Poet Series, Perth, Ontario, Canada, 1988).

Ronnie R. Brown is a freelance writer and broadcaster living in Ottawa, Ontario, Canada. The author of three books of poetry, she was the 2001 Winner of the Burrell Prize for Poetry. Her third poetry collection, *Photographic Evidence* (Black Moss Press, 2000) was short-listed for the Archibald Lampman Award for Poetry. She is the granddaughter, niece, and daughter of women who suffered from Alzheimer's disease.

LIFE WITH IRMA © 1988 Jessica Bryan
ALZHEIMER'S DISEASE © 2002 Jessica Bryan
Jessica Bryan was a legal secretary for twenty-five years until she decided she would rather read books than legal briefs. She lives in the Santa Cruz Mountains in California where she works at home writing and editing book manuscripts for herself and others.

THE DANCE © 2002 Katie Cameron
Katie Cameron was born in the Bay Area in 1945, but currently lives in Olympia, Washington where she recently retired from state government to garden, write poetry, work on long-term care issues, travel, and visit her mother in nearby assisted living. Katie's mother – a professor of human physiology – has had Alzheimer's disease for about ten years. When Katie's father died this past year, Katie made the decision to move her mother near her and into residential care. For the first time in years, Katie can visit her mother without worrying about her isolation and safety. "I lose her all over again every time I visit her," Katie says, "but I am learning to bear it, and the care is excellent."

THE BLUE DRESS © 1984 Siv Cedering
The Blue Dress was previously published in *Virginia Quarterly* and subsequently in *Letters From The Floating World, New and Selected Poems* by Siv Cedering, University of Pittsburgh Press, 1984. It was also published in *Letters From The Observatory,* Karma Dog Editions, 1998.
Siv Cedering is the author of ten collections of poetry in English and seven books of fiction written in Swedish. Her writing has appeared in over two hundred anthologies and textbooks and in many fine magazines including: *Harper's, Georgia Review, Ms., Science, The New Republic, The New York Times, Ploughshares, Partisan Review,* and *Paris Review.* She is also a painter and sculptor, and her work has been shown in galleries and museums in various parts of the country.

PASSOVER © 1987 Stephen M. Fishman
Steve Fishman teaches in the Philosophy Department at the University of North Carolina at Charlotte where he has been a faculty member since 1967. He is the co-author of three recent books about teaching and writing in the classroom: *John Dewey and the Challenge of Classroom Practice* (Teachers College Press, 1998), *Unplayed Tapes: A Personal History of Collaborative Teacher Research* (Teachers College Press, 2000), and *Whose Goals? Whose Aspirations? Learning to Teach Underprepared Writers Across the Curriculum* (Utah State University Press, 2002.)

AFTER THE VISIT OF AN ELDERLY RELATIVE
© 1987 Alice Wirth Gray

Alice Wirth Gray has had poems in *The Atlantic, The American Scholar, Poetry*, and many other places. The Cleveland State Poetry Center published her first book, *What The Poor Eat*, in 1993. She also has published short stories.

IN THE LAST PLACE © 2002 Joseph Green

Joseph Green has been teaching English at Lower Columbia College in Longview, Washington for sixteen years, during which time his poems have appeared in such publications as *The Bellingham Review, Crab Creek Review, 5 AM, Free Lunch, Hubbub, Pearl, Pontoon, Slipstream, The Threepenny Review, Wilderness, Willow Springs,* and *ZYZZYVA*. As PEN Northwest's Margery Davis Boyden Wilderness Writer for 2000, he spent seven months, alone most of the time, at the Dutch Henry Homestead in Oregon's Rogue River Canyon. That experience produced many of the poems in *The End of Forgiveness*, which won the Floating Bridge Press Poetry Chapbook Award for 2001.

SIMPLY MUST © 2002 Juley Harvey

Juley Harvey is a receptionist by day at Weider Publications, Woodland Hills, CA. *Shape, Natural Health,* and *Muscle & Fitness* are among their seven titles. For the two previous years, she served as an operator and back-up receptionist at HQ Global Workplaces, an executive office suites company in Woodland Hills. She is keeping her night job as a prize-winning poet and has published her work in more than thirty publications, both slicks and literary. She lives in the Los Angeles area with her two kitties and continues to hunt for the perfect poet, poem, man.

COMMUNION © 2002 Katie Kingston

Katie Kingston is a recipient of the Colorado Council on the Arts Literary Fellowship in Poetry. She has published her work in various literary magazines including *Puerto del Sol, Blue Mesa Review, Southwestern American Literature, Weber Studies, The Texas Observer,* and *High Country News*. She earned her MFA in Creative Writing at Vermont College in 1993 and currently teaches poetry, Spanish, and English at Trinidad State College in Colorado. As literary chairperson of the Trinidad Area Arts Council, she directs the *Corazon de Trinidad Reading Series* and also serves as poetry advisor for the *Purgatoire: A Journal of Literary and Visual Arts*. She is a participating artist in the Virtual Chautauqua Project based at CU in Boulder, which can be accessed at www. virtualchautauqua.org/katiekingston.

THE LIST © 2002 Kate LeSar

Kate LeSar is a former nursing administrator with twenty-five years of health care experience, primarily in geropsychiatry, long-term care, and international health. She has run several programs for people with dementia. *The List* is based on her first-hand experience with her mother and father-in-law. Kate lives in the Washington, D.C. metropolitan area and is currently completing a novel about family relationships in late life.

THE BLACK HOLE © 2002 Bobbi Lurie

Bobbi Lurie's stories, essays, and poems have been published in numerous magazines and anthologies in the United States and England. In addition to being a writer, she has worked as an occupational therapist, muralist, printmaker, crisis counselor, and art reviewer. Her autobiographical essay, "4 O'Clock" was recently nominated for the Pushcart Prize. She lives with her family in Santa Fe, New Mexico.

MY ALZHEIMER'S PERCUSSION BAND – unplugged version © 2002 Stephen J. Lyons

Stephen J. Lyons is the author of *Landscape of the Heart*, a single father's memoir (Washington State University Press). His prose and poetry appears in many anthologies, including *Passionate Hearts* (New World Library), *Split Verse* (Midmarch Arts Press), *Bless the Day* (Kodansha Press), *Living in the Runaway West* (Fulcrum Press), and *In Black and White: Idaho Photography and Writing* (Confluence Press). He writes full time from his home in the rural Midwest.

THAT'S WHAT IT'S ALL ABOUT
© 2002 Sue Mayfield-Geiger

Sue Mayfield-Geiger is the Editor of *Baycomber*, a Texas coastal magazine, and she works as a freelance writer and editor for other publications. She has a B.A. in English from Our Lady of the Lake University in San Antonio and is married with two grown sons and three grandchildren. Sue was born in Houston, Texas, but spent her girlhood years fishing the bay waters near Galveston with her father, who not only taught her how to bait a hook, but also how to water ski, steer an outboard motor, and find solace in the majesty of the sea, as well as many other things. Her hero, mentor, and confidante, Sue dedicates this story with love to a man, who despite his lack of formal education, knew more than anyone she's ever met. In memoriam: Clarence A. Shinn, Sr. 11/6/14 – 9/2/99

DETAILS © 1987 Thomas Michael McDade

Thomas Michael McDade lives in Monroe, CT with his wife Carol. They have no children. He is 56 years old and works as a computer programmer in the plumbing industry. He's been a dishwasher, busboy, waiter, construction worker, lifeguard, painter, roofer, janitor, landscaper, truck driver, bag-boy, and he's worked in a various mills and factories. He's managed a Waldenbooks and an insulation warehouse. He served two tours of duty in the U.S. Navy and graduated from Fairfield University, Fairfield, CT. A chapbook of his poetry titled *E Pluribus Aluminum* was published by the Liquid Paper Press, Austin, Texas. His chapbook called *Our Wounds* is in the works from the Pitchfork Press also in Austin

SPANISH ENTERS THE ROOM © 2002 Joseph D. Milosch

Joe Milosch worked for 20 years as a trail locator for the Cleveland National Forest and as a heavy equipment foreman. His poetry draws on those experiences as well as his years growing up outside of Detroit and the time he spent in the Army during the Vietnam War. His has published numerous award-winning chapbooks including: *On The Wing* (Barnes and Noble), *Father of Boards and Woodwinds* (Inevitable Press for the Laguna Poets Series), *If I Could Imagine, Among Men*, and *Now She Bends Away.* Two of his poems *Among Men* and *Letters From Paul* were nominated for Pushcart awards. He currently teaches at National University.

INTRODUCTION © 2002 Victor Molinari, Ph.D.

Victor Molinari is the Director of Psychology Training at the Houston Veterans Affairs Medical Center and a faculty associate of Baylor College of Medicine's Huffington Center on Aging. He is the former coordinator for the Psychologists in Long Term Care and the president-elect of the American Psychological Association's section on clinical geropsychology. He received the Houston chapter of the Alzheimer Association's Harry E. Walker Award for Professional Excellence. Dr. Molinari is the editor of "Professional Psychology in Long Term Care" (2000, Hatherleigh Press: New York), and has published over 75 articles in geriatric mental health journals.

THE NURSING HOME © 1988 J. David Nightingale

J. David Nightingale, Ph.D. (Physics) was born in South Africa and educated in England and Scotland. He is retired from S.U.N.Y., New Paltz, New York, after teaching there for thirty-one years.

A MARRIAGE © 1992 Carol Nolde

A Marriage was previously published in *California State Poetry Quarterly*, Autumn, 1992

Carol Nolde lives and writes in Westfield, New Jersey. She has recent work in *Whetstone* and in the anthologies *Knowing Stones: Poems of Exotic Places* and *A Christmas Collection*.

AFTER LEAVING © 2002 *Torie Olson*

After Leaving was previously published in a slightly different form as *After Leaving Earth* by Red Cedar Review and Southern Indiana Review.

Torie Olson's short fiction has been nominated for the Pushcart Prize and published in several literary magazines including *Calyx, Literal Latté, Prairie Schooner*, and most recently in *Fantasmas*, a Mexican-American anthology of supernatural stories. *After Leaving* is part of *Crazy Ladies*, Olson's collection of short stories completed through a grant from the Vermont Council on the Arts and the National Endowment for the Arts. Olson's work has also made her a finalist for the Heekin Group Foundation's Tara Fellowship, and a semi-finalist for the Sandstone Prize in Short Fiction and the New Millennium Writings Award. She has just completed her first novel, *The Dream Poppy*, which is set in Afghanistan and Vermont.

WHAT VITA'S MOTHER SAID © 2002 Rachael Perry

Rachael Perry, a native of Michigan, lives and writes in Düsseldorf, Germany. Her stories have appeared in *StoryQuarterly, South Dakota Review, River City, Our Working Lives*, and other places. She is thankful to the Writers Group at the International Library, and she is very proud of the two strong women in her family who inspired the story.

THE SAME RAIN © 2002 Norma Fain Pratt

Norma Fain Pratt, Ph.D. in History from UCLA (1976) has taught Women's History in the U.S., Jewish History, Western Civilizations, and World Civilizations at UCLA, Sarah Lawrence College, CSU, L.A., U. of Guadalajara, and the U. of Judaism, L.A. She has won fellowships from the National Endowment for the Humanities, the Littauer Fellowship in Jewish Studies, and the American Jewish Archives (Cincinnati). Her extensive publications include, *Morris Hillquit: A Political Biography of an American Jewish Socialist*, Greenwood Press, 1979; her path-finding scholarly article on Yiddish women writers, *Culture and Radical Politics: Yiddish Women Writers, 1880-1940, American Jewish History* (Summer 1980), which was anthologized *in Decades of*

Discontent (Greenwood Press, 1982 and Northeastern University Press, 1987) and reprinted in *Women of the Word: Jewish Women and Jewish Writing* (Wayne State University Press, 1994).

THE FORGETTING © 2002 Nancy Priff

Nancy Priff has written and edited more than 75 videos on medical and health-related topics as well as dozens of reference books, textbooks, and supplementary materials for health-care professionals and students. In addition to receiving professional awards for her health-care communications, her poems and short stories have been recognized by the International Library of Poetry and Montgomery County Community College. She currently lives in Ambler, Pennsylvania, with her husband John.

MOTHER-IN-LAW © 2002 Donna Pucciani, Ph.D.

Donna Pucciani received her Ph.D. in music and humanities from New York University and has taught music, humanities, English, and women's studies in high schools and colleges in the East and Midwest since 1970. The recipient of several grants from the National Endowment for the Humanities, she has done postdoctoral studies at Harvard, Loyola, Brandeis, and Ohio State Universities, respectively. Currently a writer and high school English teacher, she resides in Wheaton, Illinois. Her poems have appeared in *Maryland Poetry Review, Rockford Review, Karamu, Prairie Light Review, Konfluence, The Cape Rock, West Wind Review,* and other publications in the United States and Britain.

THE FUNERAL PARLOR © 2002 Helen Resneck-Sannes

Helen Resneck-Sannes is a psychologist in private practice in Santa Cruz, California. She also teaches and lectures nationally and internationally for the Bioenergetic Society. She is an advanced practitioner of Somatic Experiencing, type of psychotherapy for the treatment of trauma. She has published short stories and poems, as well as professional articles in psychology journals. Her story, *The Funeral Parlor*, is an excerpt from her memoir *Father's Rooms*, which invites the reader into the heart and mind of a baby-boomer daughter trying to relate to the tangled reality of a father with Alzheimer's. Writing the memoir was healing not only for herself, but her family as well. She hopes it will help others who are trying to come to terms with this disease in themselves and the people they love.

WALKS WITH MY FATHER © 1987 Elisavietta Ritchie

Elisavietta Ritchie's books include: *In Haste I Write You This Note: Stories* and *Raking The Snow* (co-winners, Washington Writers' Publishing House awards); *Flying Time: Stories* (4 PEN

Syndicated Fiction winners); *Arc of the Storm; Elegy for the Other Woman;* and *Tightening The Circle Over Eel Country* (which won the Great Lakes Colleges Association's "New Writers Award"). Ritchie's new poetry collection *Awaiting Permission to Land* recently won the Anamnesis Award.

GOD MOTHER © 1987 Candice Rowe

Candice Rowe has published short stories, including a prize-winning story, in the *Greensboro Review* and a chapbook by *Permafrost*. She has also published essays, most recently in *Red Rock Review*. Her one-act play was named a finalist in the Actors Theatre of Louisville, New Play Program and was produced Off-Off-Broadway in New York City by Love Creek Productions. She was awarded a Massachusetts Cultural Council grant for fiction. She is working on a novel set on Cape Code about a mysterious disappearance and a collection of short-shorts.

MISSING ITEMS © 1987 Zelda E. Segal

Zelda E. Segal, presently living in Asheville, North Carolina, is a former teacher, social worker, and psychotherapist. She has published poems in *Stone Country, Gravida, In Our Own Words, Inprint,* and the *Journal of New Jersey Poets.* Her nonfiction work has appeared in numerous publications, notably *The New York Times* where in 1984 her landmark essay, "My Son's Gay; That's Alright," the first on the subject, made its way to the Op Ed page. Ms. Segal is currently working on her first book of short stories and novellas.

GOTTA GO BABY DOLL© 2002 Sande Smith

Sande Smith is originally from Philadelphia, Pennsylvania. She is a poet, essayist and public relations professional living in the San Francisco Bay Area. She holds a BA in Portuguese and Brazilian Studies from Brown University and has participated in the Hurston/Wright and Voices of Our Nations Workshops for creative, non-fiction, and poetry. Sande credits her love of language to her mother, who never tired of reading out loud the musical poetry of authors such as James Baldwin, Langston Hughes, and Maya Angelou.

THE OLD MAN'S LOVE © 1991 J. J. Steinfeld

The Old Man's Love is reprinted, in a slightly different version, from *The Miraculous Hand and Other Stories* by J. J. Steinfeld.
J. J. Steinfeld is a Canadian fiction writer and playwright living in Charlottetown, Prince Edward Island, who was born in Munich, Germany, of Polish Jewish parents. He grew up in the United States and has lived most of his adult life in Canada. Steinfeld

241

has published eight short story collections: *The Apostate's Tattoo* (Ragweed Press, 1983), *Forms of Captivity and Escape* (Thistledown Press, 1988), *Unmapped Dreams* (Crossed Keys Publishing, 1989), *the Miraculous Hand and Other Stories* (Ragweed Press, 1991), *Dancing at the Club Holocaust* (Ragweed Press, 1993), *Disturbing Identities* (Ekstasis Editions, 1997), *Should the Word Hell be Capitalized?* (Gaspereau Press, 1999), *Anton Chekhov Was Never in Charlottetown* (Gaspereau Press, 2000). Steinfeld has also published a novel, *Our Hero in the Cradle of Confederation* (Pottersfield Press, 1987).

HIS UNJUST DESSERT

Bara Swain's award winning plays have been produced in New York, New Jersey, Tennessee, Missouri, and Iowa. Recent performances include a dramatic reading of selected short stories, *Your Health Comes First...You Can Always Hang Yourself Later*, (Kaufmann Theater, NYC); *Ideal Grace*, winner, Dubuque Fine Arts Players National One-Act Play Contest (IA); *You Betcha*, Lamia Ink's International One-Act Play Festival (Chez Laroe, NYC); and *Weeping Willow*, Drop Your Shorts Play Festival (Miranda Theater, NYC). Bara is the Dorsal Editor at Doorknobs & BodyPaint (www.iceflow.com).

MAGGIE © 2002 Ann G. Thomas, Ed. D.

Ann G. Thomas, Ed. D. is a Marriage and Family Therapist who writes fiction and nonfiction on aging and parenting topics. Her recent book *The Women We Become* (Prima) explores the psychological issues facing women as they age. She has owned and directed an assisted living facility in California and served on the Board of Directors for an Alzheimer's Respite Program.

DANCING IN THE WIND © 1987 Sallie Tisdale

Sallie Tisdale is working on her seventh book, a meditation on winter. Her most recent is *The Best Thing I Ever Tasted: The Secret of Food* (Riverhead, 2000). Her essays have appeared in many publications, lately in *Copis, Audubon,* and *Tin House.* She has not worked as a nurse for the past few years, since she now writes full time.

CLOSE CALLS © 2000 Pam Ullman

Pam Ullman lives and writes in Shillington, Pennsylvania. Her short fiction has been published in various literary journals. *Close Calls* won the 2000 Random House Bold Type short story contest. Pam dedicates this story to Colleen M. Hickey and her family.

TYRONE STREET © 2002 Dennis Vannatta

Dennis Vannatta has published stories in many magazines and anthologies, including *The Quarterly, Antioch Review,* and *Pushcart XV*. Two of his collections – *This Time, This place* (1991) and *Prayers For The Dead* (1994) – have been published by White Pine Press, and a new collection, *Lives Of The Artists,* is forthcoming from Livingston Press.

ST. LUKE'S GARDEN © 2002 Rhoda Waller

Lillian Waller was born in Poland in 1903, immigrated to the U.S. with her parents in 1904, and grew up in Brooklyn, NY. She loved playing piano, singing, and writing. At fifteen she went to work full-time and continued working until she retired at 65. She married and raised two daughters. After she retired, she fulfilled her dream of travel and went on her own by plane, train, bus, and freighter all over the world, including the Soviet Union and Japan. For a number of years, she wrote a weekly column for her local community newspaper, and her column on the Kent State College shooting was reprinted in the "Kent State Book." She died in 1996. She dictated *St. Luke's Garden* to her daughter, Rhoda Waller, when she was 91 years old.

Rhoda Waller is the Founding President of Timelines Community, Inc., an organization based in New York that offers presentations, workshops, and retreats for the purpose of encouraging creativity in elders. She is a Certified Seminar Leader of the Spiritual Eldering Institute, Boulder, Colorado. Rhoda holds a Master's Degree in Comparative Literature.

COMING INTO THIS WORLD © 2002 Sharon Waller

Richard T. Waller was born and grew up in rural Colorado. He received a B.A. in English, studied engineering in graduate school, and became a cartographer for the U.S. Geological Society. He traveled widely and worked in Turkey for two years. He was dedicated to concerns of social justice, education, and humane treatment of animals. He loved to read and write. *Coming Into This World* is a transcription of some of his words, spoken a few months before he died of Alzheimer's disease in loving arms.

STILL HERE © 2002 Nancy Watts

Still Here was previously published in a chapbook entitled *Working Toward Tomorrow,* from a complete book of poetry entitled *Of Ways Of Looking At A woman.*

Nancy Watts is also the author of the book *Working Toward Tomorrow.* Working under the editorial guidance of Professor Frank Anthony, Ph.D., author and founder of the New England Writers/Vermont Poets Association, Nancy is also in the process of finishing her first novel, *The River Wild.* Nancy is a wife and at-home mother of two children. Her chapbook is available from Rosecroft Publishing, 8517 Rosecroft Terrace, Ellicott City, MD 21043 for $3 plus $1 postage and handling.

I KNOW DR. ALZHEIMER © Andrew N. Wilner, MD, FACP

Andrew Wilner is a graduate of Yale University and completed a eurology residency at McGill and a fellowship in epilepsy at the Montreal Neurological Institute. He is the former medical director of the Carolinas Epilepsy Center and author of two books on epilepsy, *Epilepsy: 199 Answers (A Doctor Responds to His Patients' Questions)* and *Epilepsy in Clinical Practice, A Case Study Approach,* both published by Demos Medical Publications, Inc (www.demosmedpub.com). Dr. Wilner's fiction often focuses on the challenges faced by neurology patients and their caregivers. He is the recipient of the American Academy of Neurology's 2001 Award for Creative Expression of Human Values in Neurology for his short story, "That's It!" (may be read at www.awilner.neurohub.net). Dr. Wilner has published a number of scholarly papers on epilepsy and also writes for many medical magazines. In his spare time, Dr. Wilner enjoys sailing, windsurfing and scuba diving.

REV. ROBERT A. YOUNG © Gary Young

Gary Young is a poet and artist whose books include *Hands, The Dream of A Moral Life* and *Days.* His last book, *Braver Deeds,* won the Peregrine Smith Poetry Prize, and a new book, *No Other Life,* has just been published by Creative Arts Books. He has received fellowships from the National Endowment for the Arts and the National Endowment for the Humanities, and his print work is represented in many collections including the Museum of Modern Art and the Getty Center for the Arts. He edits the *Greenhouse Review Press.*

ORDER FORM

LOVE IS AGELESS – Stories About Alzheimer's Disease

can be ordered from:

Lompico Creek Press
P.O. Box 1403
Felton, CA 95018-1403

Please send _____ copies to:

Name: _____

Address: _____

_____

Price: $14.95 per copy $ _____

Handling & Shipping:
$3.00 for the first copy plus
$1.00 for each additional copy $ _____

California residents please add
$1.20 sales tax per copy $ _____

Total Enclosed: $ _____

Please make checks payable to: Lompico Creek Press.
Also available online at: www.loveisageless.com